Apples 2

Daily Phonics Drills

For Secondary Students

By Susan Kemmerer

Schoolhouse Publishing
659 Schoolhouse Road
Telford, Pennsylvania, 18969
(215)721-9293
www.shpublishing.com

Published by
Schoolhouse Publishing
659 Schoolhouse Road
Telford, PA 18969
(215) 721-9293
www.shpublishing.com

The Scripture quoted in **Apples 2** were taken from either the King James Version, the New King James Version, the English Standard Version or the New International Version.

The photo of the apple used on the cover is being used by permission, courtesy of the New York Apple Association® New York Apple Association.

Waiver of Responsibility

Using **Apples 2** is not a guarantee that the user will become a great speller. It is important to use **Apples 2** in conjunction with individual course work. I encourage the user to read, read, read. Using **Apples 2** in conjunction with lots of reading *will help* to cement spelling rules in the mind of the user.

Dedication

To my husband, Dale...who has believed in me and my projects, invested in them, participated in them and motivated me in the process.

Dale, this book wouldn't have been written if it hadn't been for your encouragement. I love you! God's hand is so evident in you.

...and to Jesus Christ, my Lord and Savior, who always enables me to apply creativity (even when I felt I had no creativity left) to our homeschool in each situation uniquely for each precious child He has entrusted to me.

Note to parents: I used four different versions of the Bible in creating **Apples 2** (KJV, NKJV, ESV, and NIV). Generally I chose the version that used words illustrating the spelling rule being studied. Most of the fill-in-the-Bible-verse drills have obvious answers. If the answer isn't obvious, feel free to check the answer key in the back of this book.

Introduction

Do you have a student who can't remember how to spell the most simple words? You go over the spellings of the same words again and again, but within a day he's repeating the same mistakes! His spelling tests are a disaster, and his spelling lists just keep getting longer and longer until they threaten to overwhelm! You know he's not stupid...but when it comes to spelling...well, let's just say he's challenged. If you could take him back through elementary phonics, you would – but he would be insulted by the childish work.

Enter....**Apples 2 Daily Phonics Drills for Secondary Students!**

Apples 2 simply presents approximately one spelling rule each week, encompassing many of the most important spelling rules. **Apples** does *not* dwell on the many exceptions to the rules (although there are notes provided in the back of the book explaining the exceptions). You see, if your student is a poor speller, spelling exceptions are just more confusing!

In **Apples 2**, spelling exceptions are presented in *separate* drills rather than as exceptions to the rules. This will help eliminate confusion and will help the student to concentrate on the many words that *do* follow the rules, while at the same time teaching them the odd spellings separately.

Apples 2 will help your student to become a more proficient speller by helping him through simple, short, daily drills to memorize the rules. No lists, no tests. Your student simply completes one **Apple** each day. Every tenth day is a review of previously-learned rules. And the answer key is conveniently provided in the back of the book.

If you have a poor speller, he will probably always struggle in this area – but **Apples 2** will keep phonics rules fresh in his mind and give him some of the tools he'll need to improve.

And last, but by no means least, **Apples 2** helps the student to apply the rules by completing Scripture, puzzles, and sentences, encouraging him in his faith as well in his academics.

Remember: an **Apple** a day will help to keep your spelling woes at bay!

Helps

<u>Exceptions:</u> As you know, every spelling rule has exceptions. To a poor speller, exceptions just make spelling even more confusing! For this reason **Apples 2** does not present spelling exceptions as part of the drills. Rather, **Apples 2** shows the student the many words that *do* follow the rules. If your student is doing well with the *rules*, you may choose to have him read the *exceptions* to the rules in the notes in the back of this book. (The exceptions to each rule are presented separately along with the appropriate lesson numbers for easy reference.) If, however, he is still struggling with a rule, you may choose to forego presenting the exceptions until he is more comfortable with the rule.

<u>Bible versions</u>: In creating drills for **Apples 2**, we used four Bible versions: King James Version, New King James Version, English Standard Version, and New International Version. We picked the version which used the words/rules being studied. We realize that not everyone has all four versions. As **Apples** is not intended as a Bible study, we suggest that you don't bog your student down with looking up references in four versions. Here are our suggestions:

- Tell your student that ***most of the answers will be obvious*** (each drill contains a word box or list to draw from).
- Those answers that aren't obvious can usually be figured out through the ***process of elimination***.
- Those few that are left can easily be ***looked up in the answer key***. This is actually ***encouraged***, as copying words is an excellent spelling exercise.

<u>Remember</u>: **Apples 2** is intended to be quick and easy to use (no more than ten minutes each day). By ***keeping it simple***, **Apples 2** minimizes stress in spelling, which enhances learning.

Table of Contents

Day 1

Clue: The long -a sound is usually spelled one of three ways. These spellings must be memorized:
- With an ***-ai***.
- With an ***-a*** followed by a ***silent -e*** on the end.
- If the word *ends* with the long -a sound, it is usually spelled with an ***-ay***.

Fill in the following clues with long-a-silent-e words.

bake	Dave	maze	sane
bare	Fate	Nate	space
cane	made	sale	stare
			Trade

1. The elderly gentleman walked with a ______________.
2. The ____________ shuttle, Columbia, met with disaster in 2003.
3. Their marriage was "____________ in heaven."
4. It is not polite to ________________.
5. Have you ever walked through a corn ____________ on a farm, and gotten lost in it?
6. The kids sold many toys at the yard ___________.
7. His ___________ shoulders were badly sun-burnt.
8. Monica wanted to ______________ mud pies.
9. *"The __________ of the Yellow Woodbee,"* by ___________ and Neta Jackson, is the story of the missionary ____________ Saint.
10. You have to wonder if the terrorists who flew into the ___________ Towers on Nine Eleven were entirely ___________.

Day 2

> **Clue:** The long -a sound is usually spelled one of three ways. These spellings must be memorized:
> - With an -_____ as in **train**.
> - With an -___ followed by a ***silent*** -_____ on the end, as in **save**.
> - If the word *ends* with the long -a sound, it is usually spelled with an -____.

Complete the following Bible verses with long-a words. One word is used twice.

blade	came	hates	pale
blame	faces	lame	sale
became	flames	lanes	share

1. "But whoever ___________ his brother is in the darkness and walks around in the darkness..." (1 John 2:11)

2. "There the angel of the Lord appeared to him in ___________ of fire from within a bush..." (Exodus 3:2)

3. "If I do not bring him back to you and set him here before you, I will bear the ___________ before you all my life..." Genesis 43:9

4. "Even the handle sank in after the __________, which ________ out his back....and the fat closed in over it." Judges 3:22

5. "He is to ____________ equally in their benefits, even though he has received money from the ________ of family possessions." Deuteronomy 18:8

6. "...no longer will their _________ grow ________." Isaiah 29:22.

7. "So the servant ________ and reported these things to his master. Then the master of the house _____________ angry and said to his servant, 'Go out quickly to the streets and __________ of the city, and bring in the poor and crippled and blind and ___________.'" Luke 14:21

Day 3

Clue: The long -a sound is usually spelled one of three ways. These spellings must be memorized:

- With an -_____ as in **train**.
- With an -___ followed by a ***silent*** -______ on the end, as in **save**.
- If the word *ends* with the long -a sound, it is usually spelled with an -____.

Complete the following Scriptures with **-a-silent-e-** words, then use those words to complete the crossword puzzle.

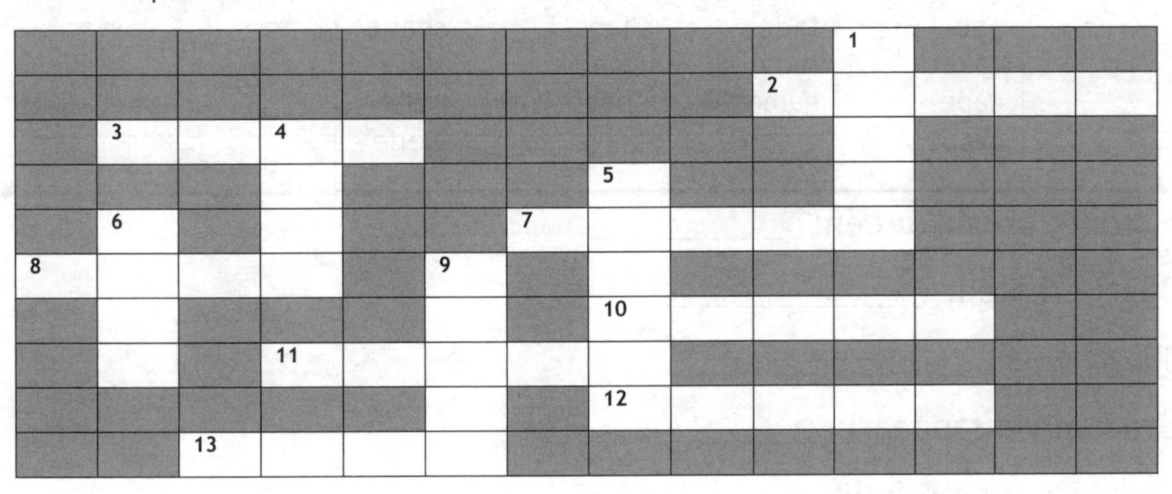

1. Prov. 19:26 "He who does violence to his father and (5 down) ________________ away his mother is a son who brings (10 across) ________________ and reproach."

2. Jeremiah 2:14 "Is Israel a (1 down)____________?"

3. Genesis 34:21 "Let them dwell in the land and (9 down)________in it."

4. Judges 16:2 "They surrounded the (2 across) ______________ and set an ambush for him all night at the (3 across)____________ of the city.

5. Isaiah 64:7 "There is no one who calls upon your (13 across) ______________, who rouses himself to (4 down)______________ hold of you; for you have hidden your (8 across)________________ from us, and have (6 down)______________ us melt in the hand of our iniquities."

6. Mark 6:11 "And if any (11 across)____________ will not receive you and they will not listen to you, when you leave, (12 across)____________ off the dust that is on your feet as a testimony against them."

7. Matthew 12:40 "For just as Jonah was three days and three nights in the belly of the (7 across)______________, so will the Son of Man be three days and three nights in the heart of the earth."

(Use these words: chases, face, gate, made, name, place, place, shake, shame, slave, take, trade, whale)

Day 4

Clue: The long -a sound is usually spelled one of three ways. These spellings must be memorized:

- With an -_____ as in **train.**
- With an -___ followed by a ***silent*** -_____ on the end, as in **save.**
- If the word *ends* with the long -a sound, it is usually spelled with an -____.

Fill in the blanks with **-a-silent-e** words.

ape	fade	jade	shade
cake	fame	made	slate
cape	game	pace	stale
drape	grade	save	wade

1. A stone, usually green: ___________
2. Built; created: ______________
3. Shaw; cloak: ________________
4. Gradually disappear: _______________
5. Popularity; notoriety: ________________
6. Soccer, chess, etc.: _______________
7. Not fresh: __________________
8. Test score: __________________
9. Stone used for chalk boards: _________________
10. Walk ankle-deep in water: __________________
11. Protected from the sun: ___________________
12. Angel food, chocolate, etc.: _________________
13. Walk back and forth, back and forth: _____________
14. Monkey, gorilla: __________________
15. Curtain: ________________
16. Rescue: ________________

Clue: The long -a sound is usually spelled one of three ways. These spellings must be memorized:

- With an -_____ as in **train**.
- With an -___ followed by a ***silent -_____*** on the end, as in **save**.
- If the word *ends* with the long -a sound, it is usually spelled with an -____.

Fill in the blanks with **-ai-** words. One word is used twice.

fails	pain	trained
gain	rain	waited
main	remain	waiting
paid	trail	

1. Chris ______________ a long time to get a job at McDonald's.
2. He was ____________ on the register and the grill.
3. His ___________ job is to run the cash register.
4. He refuses to ride his bike to work in the ___________.
5. Sometimes he takes the _________ road, and other times he takes the back _____________ to bike to work.
6. ______________ on rude customers can be a ____________.
7. Even when customers are rude, Chris never ___________ to be polite.
8. Eating all those burgers and fries has caused him to ___________weight.
9. Chris will ___________ at McDonald's until he gets his driver's license.
10. He gets ____________ every other Friday.

Day 6

Clue: The long -a sound is usually spelled one of three ways. These spellings must be memorized:

- With an -_____ as in **train**.
- With an -___ followed by a ***silent*** -_____ on the end, as in **save**.
- If the word *ends* with the long -a sound, it is usually spelled with an -____.

Complete the Scriptures with **-ai-** words. Some are used twice.

afraid	hair	sail	tails
braided	laid	saint	
faith	pair	Spain	
grain	praise	tail	

1. Matthew 17:20 "…If you have ____________ like a ___________ of mustard seed, you will say to this mountain, 'Move from here to there,' and it will move, and nothing will be impossible for you."
2. Psalm 113:1 "_____________ the LORD! ___________, O servants of the LORD!"
3. Luke 2:7 "She gave birth to her firstborn son and wrapped him in swaddling clothes and _________ him in a manger."
4. Philippians 4:21 "Greet every ____________ in Christ Jesus."
5. Acts 27:24 "Do not be __________, Paul; you must stand before Caesar…God has granted you all those who ________ with you."
6. Rom. 15:24 "I hope to see you in passing as I go to __________."
7. 1 Timothy 2:9,10 "Women should adorn themselves…with modesty and self-control, not with _____________ ___________ and gold or pearls or costly attire, but with what is proper for women who profess godliness—with good works."
8. Judges 15:4 "So Samson went and caught 300 foxes and took torches. And he turned them ________ to _______ and put a torch between each _________ of _________."

Clue: The long -a sound is usually spelled one of three ways. These spellings must be memorized:

- With an -_____ as in **train**.
- With an -___ followed by a ***silent*** **-_____** on the end, as in **save**.
- If the word *ends* with the long -a sound, it is usually spelled with an -____.

Fill in the blanks with **-ai-** words.

bait	drain	jail	pair	stairs
brain	fair	maid	raid	tail
chair	hail	mail	snail	vain

1. A worm, when you go fishing: ___________
2. Personal house cleaner: ___________
3. What you sit on: ___________
4. The end of a dog: ___________
5. Escargot: ___________
6. Letters with postage: ___________
7. Prison: ___________
8. Icy precipitation: ___________
9. A sudden, aggressive mission: ___________
10. Thinking organ: ___________
11. What water goes down: ___________
12. Proud of one's beauty: ___________
13. Couple: ___________
14. Carnival: ___________
15. Steps: ___________

Day 8

Clue: The long -a sound is usually spelled one of three ways. These spellings must be memorized:

- With an -_____ as in **train.**
- With an -___ followed by a ***silent*** -____ on the end, as in **save.**
- If the word *ends* with the long -a sound, it is usually spelled with an -____.

Complete the following Scriptures with **-ay** words. Some of the words are used more than once.

day	gray	play
delay	hay	pray
display	lay	

1. 1 Peter 2:6 "Behold, I ______ in Zion a chief cornerstone, elect, precious..."
2. Isaiah 11:8 "The nursing child shall _________ over the hole of the cobra..."
3. Matthew 6:9 "__________ then like this: Our Father in heaven..."
4. Matthew 6:11 "Give us this _________ our daily bread..."
5. Exodus 22:29 "You shall not ___________ to offer from the fullness of your harvest..."
6. 1 Corinthians 3:11-13 "For no one can ________ a foundation other than that which is laid, which is Jesus Christ. Now if anyone builds on the foundation with gold, silver, precious stones, wood, _________, straw—each one's work will become manifest, for the __________ will disclose it, because it will be revealed by fire..."
7. Psalm 19:2 "________ after ________ they pour fourth speech; night after night they ____________ knowledge."
8. Hosea 7:9 "His hair is sprinkled with _________, but he does not notice."

Clue: The long -a sound is usually spelled one of three ways. These spellings must be memorized:

- With an -_____ as in **train**.
- With an -___ followed by a ***silent*** ***-*** _____ on the end, as in **save**.
- If the word *ends* with the long -a sound, it is usually spelled with an -____.

Fill in the blanks with **-ay** words.

1. Inlet, harbor: __________
2. A blue-colored bird: ___________
3. To remove the skin by whipping: ____________
4. Homeless cat: ____________
5. Hopeless, helpless surprise: _____________
6. A donkey sound: ___________
7. A month in spring: _____________
8. Money exchange: ___________
9. Happy: __________
10. Rot away:___________
11. Used to carry food and dishes: ____________
12. To speak: ___________
13. To kill: ____________
14. Remain: ____________
15. Jesus is the ___________.
16. Battle, skirmish: ___________
17. Beam: _____________
18. Mist or stream from a bottle: ____________
19. Not home: _____________

away
bay
bray
decay
dismay
flay
fray
gay
jay
May
pay
ray
say
slay
spray
stay
stray
tray
way

Day 10 Review

Clue: The long -a sound is usually spelled one of three ways. These spellings must be memorized:

- With an -_____ as in **train**.
- With an -___ followed by a ***silent*** -_____ on the end, as in **save**.
- If the word *ends* with the long -a sound, it is usually spelled with an -____.

Fill in the words with **long-a** words. Some words are used twice.

brain	faith	grave	mare	same	snails	take
day	flare	jay	paces	saved	snakes	today
decay	gate	lay	pray	scare	spare	wait
delay	glare	made	rain	shade	tails	wake
drain		makes	remains			

1. "Now I ___________ me down to sleep. I _________ the Lord my soul to keep. If I should die before I ___________, I _________ the Lord my soul to ___________."
2. I didn't want to ____________ the little gray ___________ with the ____________ from the ____________ as I waited for Pierre to bring the _____________ tire for the buggy.
3. Reviews like this one can be quite a ___________ _____________.
4. A __________ like _____________ ___________ me want to go singing in the ____________.
5. I'll never be the ___________ again since Jesus ___________me.
6. The _____________ of the dead blue __________ will ________________ quickly in this heat.
7. ___________ on the Lord. Have ___________ in the Lord.
8. What are little boys __________ of? ___________ and _____________ and puppy dog ____________.
9. ___________ ten ____________ to the east. Go through the _____________ yard _____________. Don't ___________. You will find the treasure buried under the first ___________ tree.

Clue: Memorize this poem: "i before e except after c, or when it says a as in neighbor and weigh." This means that in words with this vowel combination...

- If the letter c is first, use an -ei.
- If the word has the long a sound, use -ei.
- The above two are uncommon, so mostly you will use an -ie.

In the words below fill in the proper vowel combination. After each word, write an A,B, or C to indicate the rule you used.

A. Use i before e in most words.
B. Use ei- if the letter c is in front of it.
C. Use ei- if the word has the long a sound.

- fr____nd _____ bel_____ve _____ th____f _____
- c____ling _____ retr_____ve _____ ____ght(8)_____
- rec____pt _____ dec____tful _____ p____ce _____
- w____gh _____ f____ld _____ y____ld _____
- n____ghbor _____ Dan____l _____ t____ _____

Circle the misspelled words in the sentences below. Write them correctly on the lines following, along with an A,B, or C on the smaller lines to indicate the rule you used.

1. We have a Golden Retreiver named Daneil. _____________ ___, ____________________ _____
2. He is ieght years old and wieghs too much to be healthy. ____________________ _____, ____________________ _____
3. All our nieghbors see him as a freind. ________________ _____, ____________________ _____
4. Sometimes he acts like a theif and sneaks a peice of meat from the table. __________________ _____, ______________ _____
5. I beleive he could jump as high as the cieling to retreive a tossed frisbee if he didn't wiegh so much! _________________ _____, ______________ ___, ______________ ___, ____________ ____
6. We've never had to tei him up, because he never wanders farther than the feild next door. ______________ ____, ______________ _____
7. There's not a decietful bone in his loyal body! ________________ ___

Day 12

Clue: Memorize this poem: "___ before ___ except after ___, or when it says ___ as in neighbor and weigh." This means that in words with this vowel combination...

- If the letter c is first, use an -_____.
- If the word has the long a sound, use -_____.
- The above two are uncommon, so mostly you will use an -____.

In the words below fill in the proper vowel combination. After each word, write an A,B, or C to indicate the rule you used.

A. Use i before e in most words.
B. Use ei- if the letter c is in front of it.
C. Use ei- if the word has the long a sound.

- l___ _____
- th____r _____
- h____r ______
- y____ld _____
- dec____ved _____
- d____ _____
- conc____ve _____
- pat____nt _____
- f____ld ______
- n____ghbor _____
- qu____t ______
- ch____f ______
- fr____nd _____
- rec____ve _____
- bel____ve _____

In the Bible verses below, use the correctly-spelled words from the above list to fill in the blanks.

1. "Behold, the virgin shall _______________ and bear a Son, and shall call His name Immanuel." Isaiah 7:14
2. "...But _____________ yourselves to God, and your members as instruments of righteousness to God." Romans 6:13
3. "The trees of the __________ shall clap their hands." Isaiah 55:12
4. "He makes me ______ down in green pastures." Psalm 23:2
5. "I write these things to you who ______________ in the name of the Son of God..." 1 John 5:13
6. "You shall love the Lord your God...and your ________________ as yourself." Luke 10:27
7. "Therefore you are...an _______ of God through Christ." Gal. 4:7
8. "Be _________________ with them all." 1 Thessalonians 5:14
9. "He...said to them, '______________ the Holy Spirit.'" John 20:22
10. "Do not be __________________, God is not mocked; for whatever a man sows, that he will also reap." Galatians 6:7
11. "Aspire to lead a _____________life, to mind your own business, and to work with your hands..." 1 Thess. 4:11
12. "A __________________ loves at all times..." Proverbs 17:17

Clue: Memorize this poem: "___ before ___ except after ___, or when it says ___ as in neighbor and weigh." This means that in words with this vowel combination...

- If the letter c is first, use an -_____.
- If the word has the long a sound, use -_____.
- The above two are uncommon, so mostly you will use an -____.

In the words below fill in the proper vowel combination. After each word, write an A,B, or C to indicate the rule you used.

A. Use i before e in most words.
B. Use ei- if the letter c is in front of it.
C. Use ei- if the word has the long a sound.

• p____ _____	rel____ved _____	th____r _____
• aud____nce _____	conc____t _____	v____w _____
• misch____f _____	f____nd ______	rev____w _____
• dec____t _____	rec____pt _____	f____rce _____
• qu____t _____	repr____ve ______	cash____r _____

Circle the misspelled words in the sentences below. Write them correctly on the lines following along with an A,B, or C to indicate the rule you used.

1. Reveiw your history before the test. _______________ _____
2. He is such a mischeif maker. __________________ _____
3. The Bible says a meek and queit spirit is beautiful.______________ ___
4. He asked for a volunteer from the audeince. ___________ ____
5. Feirce winds damaged the roof. _______________ _____
6. Thier church is growing daily. _______________ _____
7. The casheir checked the reciept to make sure the product rang up on it. _______________ _____, _________________ _____
8. Eric had to give his speech today, but he was releived when he was granted a repreive. ____________ _____, __________ ____
9. Have you ever had shoofly pei? _________________ ______
10. The feind was concieted enough to return to the crime scene. __________________ _____, ___________________ ______
11. We had a veiw of the ocean from our room!_________ _____

Day 14

Clue: Memorize this poem: "___ before ___ except after ___, or when it says ___ as in neighbor and weigh." This means that in words with this vowel combination...

- If the letter c is first, use an -_____.
- If the word has the long a sound, use -_____.
- The above two are uncommon, so mostly you will use an -_____.

In the words below fill in the proper vowel combination. After each word, write an A,B, or C to indicate the rule you used.

A. Use i before e in most words.
B. Use ei- if the letter c is in front of it.
C. Use ei- if the word has the long a sound.

• fr____ndly _____	repr____ve _____	th____r _____
• dec____tful _____	pat____ntly _____	qu____tly _____
• h____rloom _____	rel____ved _____	v____wing _____
• uny____lded _____	conc____ted _____	th____ves _____
• f____ndish _____	aud___nce _____	bel____f _____

Circle the misspelled words in the sentences below. Write them correctly on the lines following along with an A,B, or C to indicate the rule you used.

1. The old Bible, printed in 1793, was a valuable family hierloom.
   ______________ ____
2. We were releived when the feindish theives were caught.
   ____________ _____, _____________ _____, ____________ _____
3. An unyeilded heart is a decietful heart – concieted in its beleif that God is not in control. ______________ _____, ____________ _____, _____________ _____, ____________ ____
4. They chose a participant from the veiwing audeince.
   _______________ _____, _________________ _____
5. Thier freindly cat sat queitly purring on the visitor's lap. ____________ _____, _____________ _____, ____________ _____
6. Unjustly condemned, the prisoner pateintly awaited a repreive.
   ______________ _____, ______________ _____

Clue: Memorize this poem: "___ before ___ except after ___, or when it says ___ as in neighbor and weigh." This means that in words with this vowel combination...

- If the letter c is first, use an -_____.
- If the word has the long a sound, use -_____.
- The above two are uncommon, so mostly you will use an -____.

In the words below fill in the proper vowel combination. After each word, write an A,B, or C to indicate the rule you used.

A. Use i before e in most words.
B. Use ei- if the letter c is in front of it.
C. Use ei- if the word has the long a sound.

- d____t ____ exper____nce ____ ____ghteen ____
- ____ghty ____ br____fcase ____ s____ve ____
- p___rce ____ d____sel ____ n____ce ____
- s____ge ____ n____ghbor ____ th____r ____
- c____ling ____ t____rs ____ unw____ldy ____
- sh____ld ____ p____r ____ p____ty ____

Circle the misspelled words in the sentences below. Write them correctly on the lines following along with an A,B, or C to indicate the rule used.

1. When he turned ieghteen, he got a breifcase for college.
   ________________ _____, ________________ _____
2. When Mr. Glumpus went on a deit, he lost ieghty pounds.
   ________________ _____, ________________ _____
3. Satan's arrows cannot peirce the sheild of faith. ________________ _____, ________________ _____
4. My neice had a wonderful expereince on the mission trip.
   ________________ _____, ________________ _____
5. The men lowered the paralytic right through a hole in thier cieling.
   ________________ _____, ________________ _____
6. With seven teirs, the wedding cake was too unweildy to move.
   ________________ _____, ________________ _____
7. During the seige of the city, peity was common as people turned to God. ________________ _____, ________________ _____
8. There is a deisel fuel pump at the peir where we can refuel our boat.
   ________________ _____, ________________ _____
9. The nieghbor put the applesauce through a seive to get the lumps out.
   ________________ _____, ________________ _____

Day 16

Clue: How do you keep the words *was, want,* and *what* straight?

- *Was* is the past tense of the word *is.* The "uh" sound is spelled with an -a, and there is no -h-. It is a short word, just like all of the "be" verbs.
- *Want* means *desire*. It does not have an -h, nor an apostrophe. Remember: You *can't* always have what you *want*.
- *What* is one of the "5 w's" (who, what, where, when, and why). All "5 w's" begin with "wh".

Fill in the blanks with either *was, want, wanted,* or *what.*

1. Who ___________ 'standing there like a stone wall' during the Civil War?

2. Thomas "Stonewall" Jackson ______________!

3. His career ________ started when he fought in the Mexican war.

4. ___________ he really _____________ _______ to restore his family's good name.

5. ________________ _______ the outcome?

6. His military record ______ brilliant.

7. After Mexico he became a professor at Virginia Military Institute. __________ did his students think of his teaching abilities? Not much! He _______ often ridiculed as a poor teacher.

8. He didn't _________ to see the Union split, but he loved his state and believed in its sovereignty.

9. He _____ the greatest general in the South under Robert E. Lee. _________ did Lee say when Stonewall _____ accidentally shot by his own men? "You lost your left arm today, but I lost my right arm."

Clue: How do you keep the words *was, want,* and *what* straight?

- ______is the past tense of the word *is*. The "uh" sound is spelled with an __, and there is no -__-. It is a short word, just like all of the "be" verbs.
- _______means *desire*. It does not have an -__, nor an apostrophe. Remember: You ________ always have what you________.
- ________is one of the "5 w's" (who, _______, where, when, and why). All "5 w's" begin with "____".

Fill in the puzzle with the words *was, what, wanted,* and *want*.

Across

1. "He ________ wounded for our transgressions..."
3. I ____________ to be more like Jesus.
4. "_______________ a friend we have in Jesus."
6. Do you _______________ to spend eternity with Him?

Down

1. _______________ has Jesus done in your life?
2. He ____________________ the whole world to hear the Good News.
4. Do you ___________________ to get to know Him better?
5. Jesus ___________ crucified for our sins.

Day 18

Clue: How do you keep the words *was, want,* and *what* straight?

- ______is the past tense of the word *is*. The "uh" sound is spelled with an __, and there is no -__-. It is a short word, just like all of the "be" verbs.
- _______means *desire*. It does not have an -__, nor an apostrophe. Remember: You ________ always have what you________.
- ________is one of the "5 w's" (who, _______, where, when, and why). All "5 w's" begin with "____".

Use the words *what, was, want,* and *wants* in the Bible verses below.

1. 1 Chronicles 4:10 "And Jabez called on the God of Israel....so God granted him ________________ he requested."
2. Eph. 3:17-18 "That you, being rooted and grounded in love, may be able to comprehend with all the saints _________ is the width and length and depth and height – to know the love of Christ..."
3. Galatians 6:7 "Do not be deceived, God is not mocked; for ____________ever a man sows, that he will also reap."
4. Matthew 16:25 "For whoever _______________ to save his life will lose it, but whoever loses his life for me will find it."
5. Genesis 3:1 "Now the serpent _________ more crafty than any of the wild animals the Lord God had made..."
6. Genesis 1:31 "God saw all that he had made, and it ___________ very good. And there ___________ evening, and there ___________ morning – the sixth day."
7. Phil. 4:12-13 "I know _____________ it is to be in need and I know ____________ it is to have plenty. I have learned the secret of being content in any and every situation, whether well-fed or hungry, whether living in plenty or in _____________. I can do all things through Christ who strengthens me."
8. Psalm 56:4 "In God, whose Word I praise, in God I trust; I will not be afraid. ______________ can mortal man do to me?"

Clue: How do you keep the words *was, want,* and *what* straight?

- ______is the past tense of the word *is*. The "uh" sound is spelled with an __, and there is no -__-. It is a short word, just like all of the "be" verbs.
- _______means *desire*. It does not have an -__, nor an apostrophe. Remember: You ________ always have what you________.
- ________is one of the "5 w's" (who, _______, where, when, and why). All "5 w's" begin with "____".

Use the words *what, was, want, wanting* or *wanted* in the verses below.

1. "Do not be yoked together with unbelievers. For ____________ do righteousness and wickedness have in common? Or ____________ fellowship can light have with darkness?" 2 Corinthians 6:14
2. "But let patience have her perfect work, that ye may be perfect and entire, ________________ nothing." James 1:4
3. "The Lord is my shepherd, I shall not ____________." Psalm 23:1
4. "Pharoah and all his officials and all the Egyptians got up during the night, and there ________ loud wailing in Egypt, for there __________ not a house without someone dead." Exodus 12:30
5. "The young lions do lack, and suffer hunger: but they that seek the LORD shall not ________________ any good thing." Psalm 34:10
6. "Saul _____________ thirty years old when he became king, and he reigned over Israel forty-two years." 1 Samuel 13:1
7. "Finally, brothers, ___________ever is true, __________ever is noble, _____________ever is right, ___________ever is pure, ____________ ever is lovely, ____________ever is admirable—if anything is excellent or praiseworthy—think about such things. ___________ever you have learned or received or heard from me, or seen in me—put it into practice. And the God of peace will be with you." Philippians 4:8-9

8. "And when they ____________ wine, the mother of Jesus saith unto him, 'They have no wine.'" John 2:3

Day 20 Review

Clue: The long -a sound is usually spelled one of three ways. These spellings must be memorized:
- With an -____ as in **train.**
- With an -__ followed by a ***silent*** **-____** on the end, as in **save.**
- If the word *ends* with the long -a sound, it is usually spelled with an -____.

Clue: Memorize this poem: "___ before ___ except after ___, or when it says ___ as in neighbor and weigh." This means that in words with this vowel combination...
- If the letter c is first, use an -_____.
- If the word has the long a sound, use -_____.
- The above two are uncommon, so mostly you will use an -____.

Circle the misspelled words in each sentence. Write the words correctly on the lines.

1. I can't beleive you would taik the test without reveiwing first!
   ________________, ____________, ________________

2. We will recieve his promises as we wate pateintly for Him.
   ________________, ____________, ____________________

3. If we are fatheful to shair the good news of the Gospel, people will beleive and be saived. ________________, ____________, ________________, ________________

4. Prai for your family, nieghbors, and freinds. ____________, ____________________, ________________

5. Todae we cleaned the cobwebs from the cieling. We put sprai on a mop and wiped them awae. ______________, ______________, ____________, ________________

6. The kids love to plae in the feild in the rane in Mai. ____________, ____________, ____________, ____________

7. Paul said he was the cheif sinner! And this was after he was saived for decaids! ____________, ____________, ____________

Clue: The **-ou- sound** (as in the word '*out*')is usually spelled one of two ways. These spellings must be memorized:

- With an **-ou** as in **south**. *If you're not sure of the spelling and need to guess, this spelling is used about twice as often as the -ow spelling.*
- With an **-ow** as in **cow**.

Fill in the blanks with **-ou-** words.

1. The ________________ lanes of the turnpike were closed as the firefighters ____________ the car fire.
2. The successful fishing trip netted an ______________ ________________ ___________ of ___________ yesterday.
3. The cat ______________ alertly, waiting to ____________ on the unsuspecting ______________.
4. I would like to _____________, beyond a shadow of a _________, that my ______________ has never _________________ a check.
5. The watch was _____________ so tightly, the ________ hand was stuck at 4:00.
6. Poor Mr. Jinks had to remain in the ____________ resting on the _____________ with a bad case of ___________.
7. With a __________ __________, he ___________ pulled the large _____________ from the water.
8. Many ______________ have the -ou- sound, such as ___________, ___________, ___________, and _________.

astounding
bounced
couch
crouched
doubt
doused
flounder
flour
gout
hour
house
loud
mouse
mouth
nouns
ounce
pouch
pounce
pounds
proudly
shout
southbound
thousand
spouse
trout
vouch
wound

Day 22

> **Clue:** The **-ou- sound** (as in the word '*out*') is usually spelled one of two ways. These spellings must be memorized:
> - With an _____ as in **south**.
> - With an _____ as in **cow**.

Complete the following Scriptures using **-ou-** words. Some words are used more than once.

counselors	found	ground	mountains
counted	foundation	house	mouth
devoured	fountain	mountain	thousand

1. Psalm 84:10 "Better is one day in your courts than a ___________ elsewhere; I would rather be a doorkeeper in the __________ of my God than dwell in the tents of the wicked."

2. Lk. 7:9 "I have not _________ such great faith even in Israel."

3. Psalm 105:35 "And did eat up all the herbs in their land, and _______________the fruit of their _______________."

4. Psalm 87:1 "He has set his ________________ on the holy __________________."

5. Acts 19:19 "And they _____________ the value of them and ____________ it came to fifty _____________ pieces of silver."

6. Proverbs 11:14 "In an abundance of _________________ there is safety."

7. Proverbs 13:3 "Whoever guards his _______________ preserves his life."

8. Joel 3:18 "And in that day the ________________ shall drip sweet wine, and the hills shall flow with milk, and all the stream beds of Judah shall flow with water; and a ________________ shall come forth from the _____________ of the LORD and water the Valley of Shittim."

Clue: The **-ou- sound** (as in the word '*out*') is usually spelled one of two ways. These spellings must be memorized:

- With an _____ as in **south**.
- With an _____ as in **cow**.

Fill in the blanks with **-ou-** words.

1. Dog: ______________
2. Pile: ______________
3. Circular: ______________
4. Audible: ______________
5. Stick out the bottom lip: ___________
6. Road or direction: ____________
7. Knightly tournament: ______________
8. Hunch over: _____________
9. Lemons are: __________
10. Despised, rejected person: _______________
11. Despicable, disgusting: ___________
12. Dirt, earth: ______________
13. To get up on: _____________
14. Facial expression: _________________
15. Not in: ___________

countenance
foul
ground
hound
joust
mound
mount
out
outcast
pout
round
route
slouch
sound
sour

Day 24

Clue: The **-ou- sound** (as in the word '*out*') is usually spelled one of two ways. These spellings must be memorized:

- With an _____ as in **south**.
- With an _____ as in **cow**.

Complete the clues and the puzzle using **-ou-** words.

Across

1. Thee and _________.
2. Dill pickles are _________.
4. Directors, _________members.
7. Don't tell me what the movie is ____________.
8. Grumpy: _____________.
9. Sum total: ______________.
12. Hitting, bashing: _________.
14. If we believe without a ___________, we will be saved.
15. No man knows the day or ___________ when Jesus will return.

Down

1. A rainbowed fish: ___________
3. Congress may pass a law giving parents educational __________ so our education tax dollars can be spent on private or home schooled education.
4. Facial expression: __________
5. Singular of lice: ___________
6. God is _____________in mercy.
8. Rooted and ___________________
10. Lips, tongue, teeth:_________.
11. Where a kangaroo carries her: baby: ___________________
13. Fat, plump: _____________

(Word List: about, amount, council, countenance, doubt, grouchy, grounded, hour, louse, mouth, pouch, pounding, sour, stout, thou, trout, vouchers)

Clue: The **-ou- sound** (as in the word '*out*') is usually spelled one of two ways. These spellings must be memorized:

- With an _____ as in **south**.
- With an _____ as in **cow**.

Fill in the blanks with **-ow-** words. Some of the words are used more than once.

cowardly	crowds	flowers	Howard	powdery	showering	town
crowded	down	how	plowed	power	Towers	township

1. On September 11, 2001, terror rained __________ on the American people.

2. In a series of_____________ acts orchestrated by Osama Bin Laden, our nation was attacked.

3. Two jets full of fuel __________ into the World Trade ____________, ________________ debris and death onto the _______________streets of New York.

4. Another jet _____________ into the Pentagon in Washington D.C., the center of our country's military _______________.

5. A fourth jet crashed into the ground outside the small __________ of Shanksville, Pennsylvania, in Stonycreek ________________.

6. Many police and firemen, including Port Authority cop George _______________, were killed when the ______________ came crashing _____________ in a noxious cloud of ______________ dust and burning debris.

7. __________ did our nation respond to the crisis? With an outpouring of love: food, clothes, ___________ of volunteers, _____________, money, patriotism, and revival.

Day 26

Clue: The **-ou- sound** (as in the word '*out*') is usually spelled one of two ways. These spellings must be memorized:

- With an _____ as in **south**.
- With an _____ as in **cow**.

Complete the following Scriptures with **-ow-** words. Some words are used more than once.

bowed	down	plow
brow	drown	plowman
brown	drowsiness	showers
cow	flower	town

1. 1 Timothy 6:9 "They that will be rich fall into temptation...which _______________ men in destruction and perdition."

2. Proverbs 23:21 "..._____________ shall clothe a man with rags."

3. Genesis 30:35 "And he removed ...all the _____________ among the sheep, and gave them into the hand of his sons."

4. Luke 4:29 "And they...drove him out of the __________ and brought him to the __________ of the hill...so that they could throw him ______________ the cliff."

5. Isaiah 40:8 "The grass withers, the _____________ fades, but the word of our God will stand forever."

6. Ezekiel 34:26 "I will send _________ the _____________ in their season; they shall be _____________ of blessing."

7. Isaiah 11:7 "The ________ and the bear shall graze; their young shall lie ___________ together."

8. Ps. 146:8 "The LORD lifts up those who are________ ________."

9. 1 Cor. 9:10 "The ______________ should __________ in hope."

Clue: The **-ou- sound** (as in the word '*out*') is usually spelled one of two ways. These spellings must be memorized:

- With an _____ as in **south.**
- With an _____ as in **cow.**

Fill in the blanks with **-ow-** words.

1. Chunky soup: ________________
2. Angry dog sound: ________________
3. Long, formal dress: ____________
4. Small shovel: ______________
5. An exclamation: ___________
6. To bend the knee: ____________
7. To dig up for planting: ____________
8. Funny circus performer: _____________
9. Chocolate color: _______________
10. Village: ____________
11. Heifer, bull: ____________
12. Forehead: ____________
13. Sleepy: _______________
14. Fine dust, talcum: ______________
15. Strength, might: _________________

bow
brow
brown
chowder
clown
cow
drowsy
gown
growl
plow
powder
power
town
trowel
wow

Day 28

Clue: The **-ou- sound** (as in the word '*out*') is usually spelled one of two ways. These spellings must be memorized:

- With an _____ as in **south**.
- With an _____ as in **cow**.

Fill in the blanks with **-ow-** words, then find them in the puzzle below. Words may be horizontal, vertical, diagonal, forward, or backward.

- A dog sound: ______________
- Talcum: ______________
- Not brave: ______________
- Cattle: ______________
- Blooms: ______________
- Very tall building: __________
- Circus performer: __________
- Not up: ______________

-A borough: ______________
-Bathe: ______________
-Soup: ______________
-Many people: ______________
-Tool for drying: ______________
-Formal dress: ______________
-In what way? : __________
-Tiara: ______________

chowder	crowded	gown	shower
clown	crown	growl	towel
coward	down	how	tower
cows	flowers	powder	township

G	A	T	O	W	N	S	H	I	P	B	C	N
R	D	E	F	R	G	H	I	J	O	K	W	L
O	M	N	O	E	P	S	R	E	W	O	L	F
W	C	R	O	W	D	E	D	Q	D	R	S	T
L	U	V	W	O	X	Y	S	Z	E	Q	W	N
E	R	T	C	H	O	W	D	E	R	Y	U	W
I	O	P	A	S	O	S	R	L	D	R	F	O
H	O	W	G	C	H	J	A	K	E	E	N	R
L	Z	X	L	C	V	B	W	N	M	W	A	C
B	C	O	D	E	F	G	O	H	O	O	O	I
J	W	K	L	M	N	O	C	G	P	T	Q	T
N	R	S	T	U	V	W	X	T	G	U	I	L

> **Clue:** The **-ou- sound** (as in the word '*out*') is usually spelled one of two ways. These spellings must be memorized:
> - With an _____ as in **south**.
> - With an _____ as in **cow**.

In each sentence circle the misspelled words, then write them correctly on the lines following.

about	cows	hound	proudly
allowed	crowds	house's	round
around	down	jousting	shower
boughs	flour	mounted	spouse
bounded	flower	ounce	thousand
Bowser	foundation	out	towel
brow	gown	owl's	townhouse
chowder	ground	plowed	township
counted	growling	pouted	trout

1. Bauser, the hownd dog, bownded through the flour garden, grouling and barking at the crouds. ____________ ____________

____________ ____________ ____________ ____________

2. The knight mownted his steed for the first rownd of the jowsting tournament. ____________ ____________ ____________

3. Mom thickened the chouder with another ownce of flower, then added some more trowt. ____________ ____________

____________ ____________

4. Dale ploued right up to the howse's fowndation for the new flour garden. ____________ ____________ ____________ ____________

5. After her shouer Dawn wrapped the touel arownd her brou, applied her fowndation, then donned her goun. ____________ ____________

____________ ____________ ____________ ____________

6. Ben was not aloud to climb the high bows of the tree to see the oul's nest. ____________ ____________ ____________

7. His spowse powted when he told her abowt the new tounship laws prohibiting pasturing cous on less than three acres of grownd.

____________ ____________ ____________ ____________

____________ ____________

8. He prowdly cownted owt five thowsand dollars as a doun payment on the tounhowse. ____________ ____________ ______

____________ ____________ ____________

Day 30 Review

Clue: How do you keep the words *was, want,* and *what* straight?

- ______is the past tense of the word *is*. The "uh" sound is spelled with an __, and there is no -__-. It is a short word, just like all of the "be" verbs.
- _______means *desire*. It does not have an -__, nor an apostrophe. Remember: You ________ always have what you________.
- _______is one of the "5 w's" (who, _______, where, when, and why). All "5 w's" begin with "____".

Clue: The long -a sound is usually spelled one of three ways. These spellings must be memorized:

- With an -_____ as in **train**.
- With an -___ followed by a ***silent*** -______ on the end, as in **save**.
- If the word *ends* with the long -a sound, it is usually spelled with an -____.

Complete the following sentences using **long -a- words, was, want,** or **want(ed)**. Some words are used more than once.

complaint	made	praised	wait
day	motivated	rain	want
Gabe	play	take	wanted
hair	played	today	was
			what

1. ____________ _________ wrong with Stephen?

2. He couldn't _________ to help with chores.

3. He ____________ his bed and _________________ to __________ a bath and wash his _____________.

4. He _____ ________________ by having his friend, __________, come over to _____________ if he worked without _______________ and finished his school lessons.

5. We ______________ his efforts.

6. The boys enjoyed their _____________ as they _______________ in the _________________ and _____________ mud pies.

7. It also _____________ me ____________ to be young again!

Clue: The spellings for the numbers, one to twelve, must be memorized. Several of them don't follow typical spelling rules:

1 - one	**5** - five	**9** - nine
2 - two	**6** - six	**10** - ten
3 - three	**7** - seven	**11** - eleven
4 - four	**8** - eight	**12** - twelve

Write the words for numbers 1-12:

1____________	5____________	9____________
2____________	6____________	10____________
3____________	7____________	11____________
4____________	8____________	12____________

Find the words for numbers 1-12 in the puzzle below. Words may be horizontal, vertical, diagonal, forward, or backward.

Q	W	E	R	T	Y	U	I	F	O	P	E	E
A	S	I	X	S	D	T	W	O	F	G	L	V
E	E	R	H	T	H	H	J	U	K	L	E	L
Z	V	X	C	G	V	B	N	R	M	T	V	E
A	E	I	I	B	C	N	I	N	E	D	E	W
O	N	E	F	E	F	G	H	N	I	J	N	T

Day 32

Clue: The spellings for the numbers, one to twelve, must be memorized. Several of them don't follow typical spelling rules:

1 - ________	5 - ________	9 - ________
2 - ________	6 - ________	10 - ________
3 - ________	7 - ________	11 - ________
4 - ________	8 - ________	12 - ________

Answer the following questions using the words for numbers.

1. Most people have ________ legs, and most dogs have __________ legs.
2. A homonym for the "won" is the word for the number ______.
3. How many Persons make up the Godhead? ____________
4. Jonah spent __________ days in the belly of the great fish.
5. The disciples gathered ____________ baskets of scraps after Jesus fed the multitudes.
6. There are ____________ days in a week, _________ of which are considered weekend, and ________ of which are considered a typical school week.
7. God created everything in ________ days and rested on day ______________.
8. A homonym for "ate" is the word for the number ____________.
9. A baby typically grows in its mother's womb for _________ months before it is born.
10. Most people have ________ fingers and _________ toes, __________ on each hand and foot.
11. There are __________ suits in a deck of cards.
12. All I want for Christmas is my _______ front teeth.
13. There are __________ donuts in a dozen. If you ate one, there would be ____________ left.
14. There are __________ seasons in a year, ________ years in a decade, ________ sun, and ________ moon.

Clue: The spellings for the numbers, one to twelve, must be memorized. Several of them don't follow typical spelling rules:

1 - ________	5 - ________	9 - ________
2 - ________	6 - ________	10 - ________
3 - ________	7 - ________	11 - ________
4 - ________	8 - ________	12 - ________

Answer the following questions using the words for numbers.

1. How many wheels does each bike have?
   - Unicycle ______________
   - Bicycle with training wheels ______________
   - Bicycle ______________
   - Tricycle ______________
2. How many planets are in our solar system? _________
3. How many U.S. senators does each state have? ________
4. There are _________ commandments and ________ books in the Pentateuch.
5. There are __________ gospels.
6. Jesus chose ____________disciples.
7. In the parable, there were _________ foolish virgins and __________ wise virgins.
8. Jesse (King David's father) had _________ sons.
9. July is month number ___________ and November is month number _____________.
10. If you added two and four, you'd have ___________.
11. There are ___________ A.M. hours and ___________ P.M. hours.
12. After Judas hanged himself, there were _____________ disciples left.
13. You have ________ nose with _________ nostrils, ________ mouth with _________ tongue, ________ ears, and ________ eyes.

Day 34

Clue: The spellings for the numbers, one to twelve, must be memorized. Several of them don't follow typical spelling rules:

1 - ________	5 - ________	9 - ________
2 - ________	6 - ________	10 - ________
3 - ________	7 - ________	11 - ________
4 - ________	8 - ________	12 - ________

Complete the following Scriptures using number words.

1. Deuteronomy 6:4 "The Lord is __________."
2. Ecclesiastes 4:12 "Though a man might prevail against ________ who is alone, ________ will withstand him—a ___________fold cord is not quickly broken."
3. 1 Cor. 13:13 "Faith, hope, and love abide, these ___________..."
4. Mat. 14:17 "We have only ________ loaves and ________ fishes."
5. Acts 11:5 "I saw...a great sheet descending, being let down from heaven by its __________ corners..."
6. Mk. 13:27 "And he will...gather his elect from the ______winds."
7. Prov. 6:16 "There are ______ things that the Lord hates, ____________ that are an abomination to Him..."
8. 1Pet. 3:20 "__________ persons were brought safely through water."
9. Lk. 17:17 "Were not ______ cleansed? Where are the ________?"
10. Gen. 37:9 "The sun, the moon, and __________ stars bowed down to me."
11. Rev. 21:21 "And the __________ gates were ___________ pearls..."

Clue: The **-oi-** sound is spelled one of two ways. These spellings must be memorized.
- When a word ends in the sound, it is spelled **-oy** (as in **boy**)...
- When the sound is in the middle of a word, it is *usually* spelled with an **-oi-** (as in **coin**).

Fill in the blanks with **-oy** words. One word is used twice.

annoy	employ	soy
boy	joy	toy
cloy	ploy	
coy	Roy	

1. The ultrasound showed that the new baby was a __________.
2. The first three fruits of the spirit are love, _________, and peace.
3. Does your little brother or sister ever ___________ you? Do you ever ___________ them?
4. The founder and pastor of our church was ________ Allebach.
5. Her perfume is so strong, it will _______ your senses.
6. Since Vaughn was allergic to cow's milk, he had to use ______ milk on his cereal.
7. The movie star acted ______, flirting with the audience.
8. The entire meeting was a ________ to get us to the surprise baby shower.
9. The baby fussed and chewed on the ________.
10. We'll need to _____________ two more people during our busy season.

Day 36

Clue: The **-oi-** sound is spelled one of two ways. These spellings must be memorized.

- When a word _______ in the sound, it is spelled -____ (as in **boy**)...
- When the sound is in the __________ of a word, it is *usually* spelled with an -____- (as in **coin**).

Fill in the blanks with **-oi-** words. One word is used twice.

boiled	joint	oil	poisonous	voice
broiled	moist	poinsettia	soil	
coin	moisture	point	spoil	
foil	noise	poise	toils	

1. The ________-operated washing machine made a lot of _________.
2. Adding a little olive _______ to the dough makes a bread that is soft and ___________.
3. You can make a joyful ___________ to the Lord whether you have a good singing ____________ or not.
4. She exhibited such ____________ when she gave her speech.
5. Dottie _______ in the _______ every day to make her garden grow.
6. We're having ____________ potatoes and ____________ flounder for dinner.
7. Could you cover that cake with __________ so the flies don't __________ it?
8. Could you __________ to the __________ you sprained?
9. The ________________ in the bathroom caused mildew to grow.
10. The leaves of the _________________ are _______________.

Day 37

Clue: The **-oi-** sound is spelled one of two ways. These spellings must be memorized.

- When a word _______ in the sound, it is spelled -_____ (as in **boy**)...
- When the sound is in the __________ of a word, it is *usually* spelled with an -____- (as in **coin**).

Complete the clues, then the puzzle, using **-oi-** words.

Across

2. An amazing accomplishment on the battlefield: __________
5. Christmas flower: _________
7. Michigan city: ___________
9. The framing that supports your floor: _________
11. To cook under very high heat: __________
13. To cancel out: ________
14. Dirt: _________
15. How a snake rests: _________

Down

1. Ready, confident: __________
3. Use your finger to direct attention: _________
4. Dampness: ______________
5. Arsenic: ____________
6. This or that: ____________
8. Works hard: __________
10. To rot: ___________
12. Olive, motor, and canola: __________

					1									
	2		3								4			
	5													
													6	
					7		8							
9			10							11				
									12					
		13					14							
15														

broil	joist	poised
choice	moisture	poison
coiled	oil	soil
Detroit	poinsettia	spoil
exploit	point	toils
		void

Day 38

Clue: The **-oi-** sound is spelled one of two ways. These spellings must be memorized.

- When a word _______ in the sound, it is spelled -_____ (as in **boy**)...
- When the sound is in the ___________ of a word, it is *usually* spelled with an -____- (as in **coin**).

Put the following **-oi-** words in alphabetical order by writing them on the numbered lines below.

coin	Detroit	oil	voice
join	boil	foil	choice
loin	soil	toil	joist
point	spoil	poise	avoid
void	coil	noise	moist
exploit	broil	poison	moisture

1. ____________________ 13. ____________________
2. ____________________ 14. ____________________
3. ____________________ 15. ____________________
4. ____________________ 16. ____________________
5. ____________________ 17. ____________________
6. ____________________ 18. ____________________
7. ____________________ 19. ____________________
8. ____________________ 20. ____________________
9. ____________________ 21. ____________________
10. ____________________ 22. ____________________
11. ____________________ 23. ____________________
12. ____________________ 24. ____________________

Clue: The **-oi-** sound is spelled one of two ways. These spellings must be memorized.
- When a word _______ in the sound, it is spelled -_____ (as in **boy**)...
- When the sound is in the __________ of a word, it is *usually* spelled with an -____- (as in **coin**).

Use **-oy** and **-oi-** words to complete these Scriptures.

anointed		joyful
point		
boil	noise	poison
boys	oil	rejoice

1. Job 41:31 "He makes the deep ________ like a pot; he makes the sea like a pot of ______________."
2. James 2:10 "Whoever keeps the whole law but fails in one __________ has become accountable for all of it."
3. James 3:8 "No human being can tame the tongue. It is a restless evil, full of deadly ______________."
4. Zechariah 8:5 "And the streets of the city shall be full of __________ and girls playing in its streets."
5. Phil.2:2 "Complete my ______ by being of the same mind."
6. 1 Thessalonians 5:16 "_____________ evermore."
7. Psalm 100:1 "Make a ____________ _________ to the LORD."
8. Psalm 5:3 "O LORD, in the morning you hear my ___________."
9. Hebrews 1:9 " You have loved righteousness and hated wickedness; therefore God, your God, has ______________ you with the _________ of gladness..."

Day 40 Review

Clue: The **-ou- sound** (as in the word '*out*') is usually spelled one of two ways. These spellings must be memorized: • With an _____ as in **south.** • With an _____ as in **cow.**
Clue: Memorize this poem: "___ before ___ except after ___, or when it says ___ as in neighbor and weigh." This means that in words with this vowel combination... • If the letter c is first, use an -_____. • If the word has the long a sound, use -_____. • The above two are uncommon, so mostly you will use an -____.

Circle the misspelled **-ou-**, **-ow**, **-ie-**, and **-ei-** words in each sentence, then spell them correctly on the lines following.

1. In our tounship, owr kids join with many other freinds and nieghbors to play soccer. _______________ __________ _____________ __________________

2. The crouds on the sidelines showt for thier favorite players as balls fly and bownce all over the feilds. ______________ _____________ ___________ _____________ _____________

3. Each mother prowdly beleives her child is the star player for the team. _________________ __________________

4. The coaches are busy cownseling the kids abowt the best ways to retreive the ball from the other team. ______________ ________________ ________________

5. The players must exhibit good sportsmanship: no powting, bad-mowthing, or decietfulness alloued. ___________ _____________ ________________ ____________________

6. The great amownts of energy running through the viens of these kids is always astownding! _____________ ___________ ______________________

Clue: If you are adding a suffix (ending) to a word that...

- Ends with a single consonant **AND**
- Has a short vowel sound

...Then you double the final consonant before adding the suffix. Some common suffixes that are added are **-ed, -ing,** and **-en.** Don't forget to double the final consonant of a short-vowel word before adding these suffixes!

Add the given suffixes to the following words:

Verb	*-ed*	*-ing*
slip	slipped	slipping
pat		
clap		
skip		
hop		

Use the words from the chart above to complete the sentences below:

1. The crowd was cheering and ______________ their hands, shouting for the singer to sing another song.
2. The little sea gull ____________ around on one foot, its other foot crippled and useless.
3. Benjamin absently _____________ the dog on the head while he talked on the phone.
4. The little girls were ______________ across the playground to the song, "Skip to my Lou."
5. The doctor quickly ____________ on his surgical gloves before touching the injured man.

Add the suffix **-ing** to each of the words below by writing out the entire word. Some of the words will not have their endings doubled. Remember the clue!

chat	sing	sleep
hang	clip	slap
part	ship	shop
spit	feel	trim

Day 42

Clue: If you are adding a ____________________to a word that...
- ❖ Ends with a single ______________________**AND**
- ❖ Has a ___________ vowel sound,

...then you ______________________ the final consonant before adding the suffix.

1. Add the given suffixes to the following words:

Verb	*-ed*	*-ing*
grab		
mop		
bud		
wed		

2. In the story below are a number of short-vowel-with-a-suffix words that have been misspelled. Draw a line through any misspelled words and write the correct spelling on the lines below:

In the parable of the Prodigal Son, the youngest son demanded his inheritance immediately. His father sadly sliped the money into a leather bag, and handed it to his son. The young man claped his hands, and grabed the money. Hoping onto the back of a donkey, he slaped its rump and took off. It wasn't long before he spent all his inheritance. It sliped through his fingers like water. He had to go beging for food, and finally took a job sloping pigs. Finally he realized he had been very foolish. Humbly he returned home and beged his father to forgive him. His father huged him and kissed him and welcomed him home.

________________ ________________ ________________
________________ ________________ ________________
________________ ________________ ________________
____

Clue: If you are adding a ____________________ to a word that...
- Ends with a single ___________________________ **AND**
- Has a ____________ vowel sound,

...then you ____________________________ the final consonant before adding the suffix.

1. Add the given suffixes to the following words:

Verb	*-ed*	*-ing*
club		
sub		
pin		
trip		
jam		

2. The following words do **not** have the endings doubled when adding a suffix. In the blanks next to each word write an A to indicate reason A, or write a B to indicate reason B.

   A. This word does not have a short vowel sound.
   B. This word does not end in a single consonant.

___bumped	___peeled	___bringing
___steeling	___raised	___helping
___sleeping	___ranted	___resting
___snowing	___gained	___coiled

Day 44

Clue: If you are adding a ____________________ to a word that...
- ❖ Ends with a single ____________________**AND**
- ❖ Has a ____________ vowel sound,

...then you ____________________ the final consonant before adding the suffix.

1. The same rule applies to many words with more than one syllable **if** the *final syllable* has a short vowel sound **and** ends with a single consonant. Add the suffix **-ing** to the following words:

compel____________	upset____________
forget____________	baby-sit____________
kidnap____________	expel____________
combat____________	abut____________
abet____________	commit____________
hobnob____________	humbug____________

2. Rewrite the following words, adding the *appropriate* **-ed** ending.

rap	pat	cap
kick	clip	rock
knot	clump	skin
pull	chap	shop
chill	check	bib

Clue: If you are adding a ____________________ to a word that...
- Ends with a single ___________________________**AND**
- Has a _____________ vowel sound,

...then you _______________________________ the final consonant before adding the suffix.

There are 2 misspelled words in each sentence. Circle them and write them correctly on the lines below.

1. At the political rally the people were claping their hands and wavving American flags.
2. Verna was efficiently diging up her tulip bulbs and was planning on poting them in the spring.
3. We choped some firewood to take campping with us.
4. We should be forgeting what is behind and strivving for what is ahead.
5. Cody chiped his knife blade while he skined the buck.

___ ______________________ ___ ______________________
___ ______________________ ___ ______________________
___ ______________________ ___ ______________________
___ ______________________ ___ ______________________
___ ______________________ ___ ______________________

On the short line in front of each of the ***above*** ten words, write the letter of the reason why the word was wrong. The reasons are listed below.

A. This word has a short vowel and ends in a single consonant, so the final consonant should be doubled.
B. This word ends with two consonants, so it shouldn't be doubled.
C. This word has a long vowel sound, so it shouldn't be doubled.

Add the given suffixes to the following words:

Verb	***-ed***	***-ing***
slug		
chip		
rob		
strum		

Day 46

Clue:

- When you are adding a suffix (ending) to a word that *ends in* "y", you should **change** the **"y"** to an **"i"**, *then* add the suffix.
- When you are adding a suffix (ending) to a word that **ends in a vowel plus "y"**, *do not change the "y" to an "i"*, or you'll have too many vowels in a row.
- When you are adding the **suffix -ing** to a word that ends in -y, *do not change the "y" to an "i"*, or you'll have two i's in a row.

In the words below, first complete the rule, then apply the rule to change the given words.

1. To add the suffix ***-ed*** to a word ending with **"y"**, change the ____ to an ____, and add ________.
   - baby________ carry________
   - marry________ bury________
   - hurry________ tarry________
   - worry________ cry________
   - accompany________ occupy________
   - sanctify________ justify________
   - pretty________ dirty________
2. To add the suffix ***-er*** to a word ending with **"y"**, change the _____ to an _____, and add _________.
   - merry________ runny________
   - carry________ happy________
   - heavy________ sloppy________
   - stinky________ pretty________
   - lovely________ ugly________
   - fluffy________ dirty________
   - friendly________ stubby________
3. To add the plural suffix ***-es*** to a word ending with **"y"**, change the ___ to an ______, and add _________.
   - baby________ cry________
   - spy________ lady________
   - family________ party________
   - puppy________ mommy________
   - penny________ hippy________
   - lobby________ cabby________
   - company________ industry________
   - enemy________ city________

Clue: When you are adding a suffix (ending) to a word that ends in "___", you should change the "____" to an "____", *then* add the__________.

In the words below, first complete the rule, then apply the rule to change the given words.

1. To add the suffix ***-est*** to a word ending with ***"y"***, change the _____ to an _____, and add _________.
   - merry________________ runny________________
   - grouchy________________ happy________________
   - heavy________________ sloppy________________
   - stinky________________ pretty________________
   - lovely________________ ugly________________
   - fluffy________________ dirty________________
   - friendly________________ stubby________________
   - funny________________ dizzy________________

2. To add the plural suffix ***-es*** to a word ending with ***"y"***, change the ___ to an ______, and add _________.
   - candy________________ strawberry________________
   - cherry________________ fly________________
   - pony________________ pansy________________
   - belly________________ story________________
   - buggy________________ reply________________
   - pity________________ satisfy________________

Circle the misspelled words in the sentences below, then write the correct spellings on the blanks following each sentence.

3. The strawberrys were ripe and the blossoms on the trees promised an abundant crop of cherrys. ____________ __________

4. The lovelyest little ponys were used to pull the colorful buggys in the parade. _____________ ______________ ______________

5. The butcher shop was the dirtyest I had seen with flys clustered thickly on the cuts of meat. ________________ ________________

Day 48

> **Clue:**
> - When you are adding a suffix (ending) to a word that **ends in a vowel plus "y"**, *do not* __________ *the "___" to an "__"*, or you'll have too many vowels in a row.
> - When you are adding the **suffix -ing** to a word, *do not* __________ *the "___" to an "____"*, or you'll have two i's in a row.

In the words below, first complete the rule, then apply the rule to correctly spell the word.

1. To add the suffix ***-ed*** to a word ending in a ***vowel* + *y***, do not __________ the ___ to an ***i***, or you'll have too many _________. Just add the suffix.
   - play __________ fray __________
   - deploy __________ gray __________
   - employ __________ stray __________
   - monkey __________ money __________
   - honey __________ toy __________
   - pray __________ replay __________
   - obey __________ enjoy __________

2. To add the suffix ***-er*** to a word ending in a ***vowel* + *y***, do not __________ the ____ to an *-i*, or you'll have too many _________. Just add the suffix.
   - play __________ spray __________
   - gray __________ buy __________
   - display __________ pray __________

3. To add the plural suffix ***-s*** to a word ending in a ***vowel* + *y***, do not __________ the ____ to an ***-i***. Just add the ***-s***.
   - play __________ fray __________
   - bay __________ key __________
   - spray __________ stray __________
   - monkey __________ donkey __________
   - honey __________ toy __________
   - pray __________ guy __________
   - trolley __________ obey __________
   - joy __________ chimney __________
   - valley __________ repay __________

Clue:

- When you are adding a suffix (ending) to a word that **ends in "___"**, you should *change the "____" to an "____", then add the__________.*
- When you are adding a suffix (ending) to a word that **ends in a vowel plus "y"**, *do not* __________ *the "___" to an "__"*, or you'll have too many vowels in a row.
- When you are adding the **suffix -ing** to a word that ends in -y, *do not* __________ *the "___" to an "____"*, or you'll have two i's in a row.

1. Add an **-ing** to the following words that end with a -y. Remember *not* to change the -y to an -i, or you'll have too many -i's in a row.

word	*-ing*	*word*	*-ing*
play		pay	
spray		pray	
obey		fray	
stray		toy	
replay		enjoy	
display		gray	
copy		try	
justify		cry	
hurry		carry	
marry		fly	
accompany		ferry	
employ		bury	
pity		party	

2. Fill in the rules for adding suffixes to words ending in -y.

- When a word ends with -y, you must change the ____ to an _____ before adding the suffix.
- When a word ends with a vowel + y, do _____ change the _____ to an ______ before adding the suffix or you will have too many ________________ in a row.
- When adding the suffix –ing to any word ending with a -y, do ____ change the _____ to an _____, or you'll have too many ____'s in a row.

Day 50 Review

Clue:

- When you are adding a suffix (ending) to a word that **ends in "___"**, you should *change the "____" to an "____", then add the___________.*
- When you are adding a suffix (ending) to a word that **ends in a vowel plus "y"**, *do not* ___________ *the "___" to an "__"*, or you'll have too many vowels in a row.
- When you are adding the **suffix -ing** to a word that ends in -y, *do not* ___________ *the "___" to an "____"*, or you'll have two i's in a row.

Clue: If you are adding a ________________ to a word that...

❖ Ends with a single ________________________**AND**

❖ Has a ___________ vowel sound,

...then you ______________________________ the final consonant before adding the suffix.

Complete the following rules for adding suffixes.

- When a word ends with -y, you must change the ____ to an _____ before adding the suffix.
- When a word ends with a vowel + y, do _____ change the _____ to an ______ before adding the suffix or you will have too many _________________ in a row.
- When adding the suffix -ing to any word ending with a -y, do ____ change the _____ to an _____, or you'll have too many ____'s in a row.
- If you are adding a ___________________ to a word that...
  ❖ Ends with a single ______________________**AND**
  ❖ Has a ___________ vowel sound, then you ____________________ the final consonant before adding the suffix.

Add the appropriate ending to each word below:

Word	*-s or -es*	*Word*	*-ing*	*Word*	*-ed*
monkey		carry		pat	
kitty		hurry		slip	
pony		hop		jump	
baby		tip		pop	
Sunday		pity		check	

Clue: The **long -o** sound in the ***middle*** of a word is usually spelled one of two ways:

- An **-o** with a **silent -e** on the end (as in *hope*).
- An **-oa** (as in *coat*).

If the word ***ends*** with a **long -o** sound, it is usually spelled with an **-ow** (as in *snow*). Occasionally it is spelled with an **-o** (as in *go* and *no*) or an **-oe** (as in *toe*).

Complete the definitions with **-o-silent-e-** words.

1. To blow up: ________________
2. When food is lodged in the throat: ______________
3. To pet: ______________
4. Past tense of "ride": ______________
5. Edible container for ice cream: ___________________
6. Thorny flower: ______________
7. A covering for pajamas: _______________
8. An area of organized trees: __________________
9. What a skeleton is made of: ___________________
10. A blind, mouse-like animal: ______________
11. Head of the Catholic church and his city:__________, _________
12. Gadget for turning channels without getting up: ______________
13. Spice similar to cinnamon: _______________
14. A short letter: ________________
15. The side or angle of a hill: ________________

bones
choke
cloves
cone
explode
grove
mole
note
pope
remote
robe
rode
Rome
rose
slope
stroke

Day 52

Clue: The **long -o** sound in the ***middle*** of a word is usually spelled one of two ways:

- An ___ with a **silent** ____ on the end (as in *hope*).
- An ______ (as in *coat*).

If the word ***ends*** with a **long -o** sound, it is usually spelled with an -____ (as in *snow*). Occasionally it is spelled with an -__ (as in *go* and *no*) or an -____ (as in *toe*).

Complete the clues, then complete the puzzle.

Across

1. To spoil with love: ________
4. By yourself: ___________
5. Past tense of weave: ________
6. To guess: _____________
8. Not these: _____________
11. From memory: ___________
15. To cast a choice: _________
16. Flexible tube to direct water: __________
17. Brass instrument: ___________

Down

2. Bell invented it: ___________
3. Small, protected bay: _______
5. Past tense of write: ________
6. Flashing light: __________
7. Past tense of strive: ________
9. Past tense of stride: ________
10. Copy exact words: _________
12. Bag, carryall: __________
13. Dwelling, home: ___________
14. Elf-like creature: __________

abode	gnome	strobe	telephone	vote
alone	hose	strode	those	wove
cove	quote	strove	tote	wrote
dote	rote	suppose	trombone	

Clue: The **long -o** sound in the ***middle*** of a word is usually spelled one of two ways:

- An ___ with a **silent** ____ on the end (as in *hope*).
- An ______ (as in *coat*).

If the word ***ends*** with a **long -o** sound, it is usually spelled with an -____ (as in *snow*). Occasionally it is spelled with an -__ (as in *go* and *no*) or an -____ (as in *toe*).

Circle the misspelled **-o-silent-e** words in the Scriptures below, then write them correctly on the lines following. Some words are used more than once.

alone	chose	rose
bones	close	smoke
broke	home	stones
broken	hope	throne
	ropes	

1. Daniel 8:7 "I saw him come cloas to the ram, and he...broak his two horns." ________________ ________________
2. Revelation 9:2 "From the shaft roas smoak like the smoak of a great furnace." ____________ ____________ ____________
3. Romans 4:18 "In hoap he believed against hoap..." ___________
4. 1 Cor.14:35 "...Let them ask their husbands at hoam."_________
5. 1 Samuel 17:40 "Then he...choas five smooth stoans from the brook..." ______________ ________________
6. Jud. 16:12 "Delilah took new roaps and bound him..."__________
7. Psalm 86:10 "You aloan are God." _____________
8. Psalm 51:8 "Let the boans that you have broaken rejoice." ________________ _______________
9. Hebrews 4:16 "Let us then with confidence draw near to the throan of grace, that we may receive mercy..." _____________

Day 54

Clue: The **long -o** sound in the ***middle*** of a word is usually spelled one of two ways:

- An ___ with a **silent** ____ on the end (as in *hope*).
- An ______ (as in *coat*).

If the word ***ends*** with a **long -o** sound, it is usually spelled with an -____ (as in *snow*). Occasionally it is spelled with an -__ (as in *go* and *no*) or an -____ (as in *toe*).

Fill in the blanks with **-oa-** words.

1. Cooked bread: ____________
2. Burden: ____________
3. Like a frog: ____________
4. A type of tree: ____________
5. Cleansing agent: ____________
6. Grain used in cereal: ____________
7. A girl's name: ____________
8. Wild pig: ____________
9. The sound a frog makes: ____________
10. Borrowed money: ____________
11. To swell up: ____________
12. Prank, scam: ____________
13. Esophagus, tongue, etc.: ____________
14. Water barrier around a castle: ____________
15. A water vehicle: ____________

bloat
boar
boat
croak
hoax
Joan
load
loan
moat
oak
oats
soap
throat
toad
toast

Clue: The **long -o** sound in the ***middle*** of a word is usually spelled one of two ways:
- An ___ with a **silent** ____ on the end (as in *hope*).
- An ______ (as in *coat*).

If the word ***ends*** with a **long -o** sound, it is usually spelled with an -____ (as in *snow*). Occasionally it is spelled with an -__ (as in *go* and *no*) or an -____ (as in *toe*).

Fill in the Scriptures with **-oa-** words.

bemoan	coasting	foams	oar
cloak	coat	goads	oath
coal	foal	goat	

1. Acts 27:8 "____________ along it with difficulty, we came to a place called Fair Havens..."
2. Isaiah 6:6 "One of the seraphim flew to me, having in his hand a burning __________..."
3. Matthew 5:40 "And if any man will sue thee at the law, and take away thy _________, let him have thy ___________ also."
4. Ecclesiastes 12:11 "The words of the wise are like __________."
5. Leviticus 16: 15 "Then he shall kill the __________ of the sin offering that is for the people..."
6. Nahum 3:7 "Who will ______________ her?"
7. Hebrews 7:21 "This one was made a priest with an _________."
8. Eze. 27:29 "From their ships come all who handle the _______."
9. Matthew 21:5 "Behold, your king is coming to you, humble, and mounted on...the __________ of a beast of burden."
10. Lk. 9:39 "It convulses him so that he _________ at the mouth."

Day 56

Clue: The **long -o** sound in the ***middle*** of a word is usually spelled one of two ways:

- An ___ with a **silent** _____ on the end (as in *hope*).
- An ______ (as in *coat*).

If the word ***ends*** with a **long -o** sound, it is usually spelled with an -____ (as in *snow*). Occasionally it is spelled with an -__ (as in *go* and *no*) or an -____ (as in *toe*).

Complete the clues below with **-oa-** words, then find those words in the word search puzzle. Answers may be horizontal, diagonal, vertical, forward or backward.

1. Wandering: ____________
2. What cork does: ____________
3. Malicious win: ____________
4. Street: __________
5. What eagles do: ___________
6. To beg: ___________
7. Bread: ____________
8. Totally wet: ____________
9. Bragging: ____________
10. Beef cut: ____________
11. Soccer score: ____________
12. Mill stone sound: ___________
13. Lion sound: ___________
14. Cooked bread: ____________
15. Sound of pain: ___________
16. Hot cereal: ______________

q	w	e	r	t	y	u	i	o	p	a	o	s
s	d	f	g	h	j	k	l	l	z	x	a	c
r	o	a	r	c	v	d	b	n	m	q	t	w
e	r	t	t	y	u	e	i	n	a	o	m	j
j	b	k	l	s	z	k	x	c	v	b	e	f
c	o	a	x	n	a	a	m	t	q	r	a	w
e	a	r	t	y	u	o	i	a	o	o	l	p
a	s	d	s	f	g	s	r	o	l	a	h	t
j	t	k	o	p	t	l	z	l	x	d	c	o
v	i	r	o	a	m	i	n	g	b	n	m	a
q	n	s	o	a	r	w	e	o	r	t	y	s
u	g	l	p	i	o	a	s	a	d	f	g	t
h	f	n	a	o	r	g	j	l	k	l	z	x

boasting	goal	oatmeal	roast
coax	groan	road	soaked
floats	loaf	roaming	soar
gloat	moan	roar	toast

Day 57

Clue: The **long -o** sound in the ***middle*** of a word is usually spelled one of two ways: • An ___ with a **silent** ____ on the end (as in *hope*). • An ______ (as in *coat*). If the word ***ends*** with a **long -o** sound, it is usually spelled with an -____ (as in *snow*). Occasionally it is spelled with an -__ (as in *go* and *no*) or an -____ (as in *toe*).

Fill in the blanks with words that end in the **long -o** sound.

1. Flakes: ____________
2. To hide or store: ____________
3. Toy that goes up and down: ____________
4. Black bird: ____________
5. Enemy: ____________
6. To understand: ____________
7. Ribbon: ____________
8. Farm tool: ____________
9. Not stop: ____________
10. To exhibit: ____________
11. Joseph: ____________
12. To pull behind: ____________
13. Professional: ____________
14. To run like water: ____________

bow crow foe flow go hoe Joe know pro show snow stow tow yoyo

Day 58

> **Clue:** The **long -o** sound in the ***middle*** of a word is usually spelled one of two ways:
> - An ___ with a **silent** ___ on the end (as in *hope*).
> - An ______ (as in *coat*).
>
> If the word ***ends*** with a **long -o** sound, it is usually spelled with an -____ (as in *snow*). Occasionally it is spelled with an -__ (as in *go* and *no*) or an -____ (as in *toe*).

Fill in the blanks with words that end in the **long -o** sound.

1. To hurl: ___________
2. What you do to a balloon: ____________
3. At the end of your foot: _________
4. To shine: ____________
5. Status: ___________
6. Not yes: ____________
7. Get bigger: _____________
8. Not high: ____________
9. "Oh, ___________ is me!"
10. To cut grass: ___________
11. Column, aisle: _____________
12. "Jesus loves me, this I know, for the Bible tells me ________."
13. To plant seed: ___________
14. Not fast: ____________

blow
glow
grow
low
mow
no
quo
row
slow
so
sow
throw
toe
woe

Clue: The **long -o** sound in the ***middle*** of a word is usually spelled one of two ways:

- An ___ with a **silent ___** on the end (as in *hope*).
- An ______ (as in *coat*).

If the word ***ends*** with a **long -o** sound, it is usually spelled with an -____ (as in *snow*). Occasionally it is spelled with an -__ (as in *go* and *no*) or an -____ (as in *toe*).

Complete the following Scriptures with **long -o-** words. Some words are used more than once.

bemoan	goat	spoken
cloak	know	swore
coasts	oath	those
foams	remote	throws
go	smote	whole

1. 2 Kings 10:32 "In __________ days...Hazael __________ them in all the ____________ of Israel."
2. Jn. 15:22 "If I had not come and ___________ to them, they had not had sin: but now they have no ___________ for their sin."
3. Dan. 8:5 "A _________ came from the west across the face of the _____________ earth..."
4. Lev. 16:22 "The __________ shall bear all their iniquities on itself to a ______________ area, and he shall let the __________ _______ free in the wilderness."
5. Jeremiah 15:5 "Who shall ___________ thee?"
6. Gn. 26:3 "I will establish the _______ I _________ to Abraham."
7. Matthew 26:72 "He denied it with an __________: 'I do not __________ this man.'"
8. Mark 9:18 "It ___________ him down, and he _____________ and grinds his teeth and becomes rigid."

Day 60 Review

Clue: The **-oi-** sound is spelled one of two ways. These spellings must be memorized.
- When a word _______ in the sound, it is spelled -____ (as in **boy**)...
- When the sound is in the __________ of a word, it is *usually* spelled with an -___- (as in **coin**).

Clue: The spellings for the numbers, one to twelve, must be memorized. Several of them don't follow typical spelling rules:

1 - _________	5 - _________	9 - _________
2 - _________	6 - _________	10 - _________
3 - _________	7 - _________	11 - _________
4 - _________	8 - _________	12 - _________

Complete the following sentences using **number words** and **-oi- words.** One word is used twice.

1. ___________ weeks before Christmas, right after Halloween, the ___________ and girls were making lists of ___________.

2. In December, month number ___________, trees were decorated with gold ___________ stars, and lights were ______________ through the branches.

3. Carolers sang "We ___________ Kings," and "________ to the World."

4. It seems as though the whole world ______________ during the ___________ weeks of advent.

5. Each _____________ is making a ______________ ___________ to the one born to save us.

6. _________ parents, ________ Child, the ____________ breath of cows, a manger on a ___________floor - these formed his _____________ bed chamber.

boys	four	noise	soil	two
coiled	Joy	One	three	voice
eight	joyful	rejoices	toys	
foil	moist	royal	twelve	

Clue: The **short -o-** sound (as in *law*) is often spelled one of two ways. These must be memorized.

- With an **-au-** (as in *author*)
- With an **-aw-** (as in *fawn*)

Fill in the blanks with **-au-** words.

1. To carry or lug: ____________
2. In a position of leadership: __________________
3. To clap in approval: ________________
4. Too colorful and decorated: ______________
5. A very poor person: __________________
6. Past tense of *teach*: _________________
7. Past tense of *catch*: _________________
8. Car pollution: _________________
9. Carefulness: __________________
10. Serious physical or emotional injury: _________________
11. A hesitation or brief stop: _________________
12. Sick to the stomach: _________________
13. Gravy: _________________
14. The writer or originator: __________________
15. Where your water comes out: ___________________

applaud
author
authority
caught
caution
exhaust
faucet
gaudy
haul
nauseous
pauper
pause
sauce
taught
trauma

Day 62

> **Clue:** The **short -o-** sound (as in *law*) is often spelled one of two ways. These must be memorized.
> - With an ______ (as in *author*)
> - With an ______ (as in *fawn*)

Complete the clues with **-au-** words, then find the words in the puzzle below. Words may be forward, backward, horizontal, diagonal, or vertical.

1. Clap hands: ____________
2. Believable: ____________
3. Steam room: ____________
4. Phrase: ____________
5. Cheese cloth: ____________
6. Corrosive: ____________
7. Tight: __________
8. To make happen: __________
9. To dab: __________
10. Carefulness: __________
11. Extremely tired: __________
12. Ornament: __________

q	w	g	a	u	z	e	e	r	t	u	e
y	c	a	u	t	i	o	n	i	o	l	s
d	a	u	b	p	a	s	d	f	b	p	u
g	u	h	j	k	l	z	x	i	i	c	a
v	s	b	n	m	q	w	s	a	e	r	l
t	e	y	u	i	o	u	d	n	p	a	c
s	d	f	g	t	a	g	h	u	j	a	k
l	z	x	c	l	u	v	b	a	u	n	m
q	w	a	p	p	l	a	u	s	e	e	r
t	e	x	h	a	u	s	t	e	d	y	u
i	o	p	a	s	d	i	f	g	h	j	k
l	z	c	v	b	c	e	l	b	u	a	b

applause	caution	gauze
bauble	clause	plausible
cause	daub	sauna
caustic	exhausted	taut

Clue: The **short -o-** sound (as in *law*) is often spelled one of two ways. These must be memorized.

- With an ______ (as in *author*)
- With an ______ (as in *fawn*)

Complete the following Scriptures with **-aw-** words. Some words are used more than once.

awesome	jaw	saw
awl	law	straw
dawns	paw	
draw	raw	

1. Psalm 66:3 "Say to God, 'How ____________ are your deeds.'"
2. Ex. 21:6 "His master shall bore his ear through with an ______."
3. Jm. 4:8 "_______ near to God, and He will ______ near to you."
4. 2 Peter 1:19 "...Until the day _________ and the morning star rises in your hearts..."
5. Job 41:2 "Can you...pierce his _______ with a hook?"
6. Isaiah 65:25 "The lion shall eat _________ like the ox."
7. Lev. 13:15 "_________ flesh is unclean."
8. Isaiah 6:1 "I ________ the Lord sitting upon a throne."
9. Matthew 5:17 "I have not come to abolish the _________..."
10. 1 Samuel 17:37 "The LORD who delivered me from the ________ of the lion and from the ________ of the bear will deliver us..."

Day 64

Clue: The **short -o-** sound (as in *law*) is often spelled one of two ways. These must be memorized.

- With an ______ (as in *author*)
- With an ______ (as in *fawn*)

Complete the following definitions with **-au-** words.

1. The eighth month: ______________
2. Misbehaved: ______________
3. Genuine: ______________
4. Female offspring: ______________
5. Seasoned pork in casing: ______________
6. To stroll: ______________
7. Blame: ______________
8. The fall season: ______________
9. Too difficult: ______________
10. Noticeably important: ______________
11. To add to or help: ______________
12. A reason why: ______________
13. Difficulty doesn't dissuade: ______________
14. Without blame: ______________
15. Author of epistles (both old name and new): ___________, ___________

augment
August
auspicious
authentic
autumn
because
daughter
daunting
fault
faultless
naughty
Paul
Saul
saunter
sausage
undaunted

Clue: The **short -o-** sound (as in *law*) is often spelled one of two ways. These must be memorized.

- With an ______ (as in *author*)
- With an ______ (as in *fawn*)

Complete the following Scriptures with **-au-** and **-aw-** words, then use them to complete the puzzle.

- Luke 12:53 "...Mother-in-_____(1 across) against her __________-in law...(7 across)"
- Titus 2:14 "He gave himself...to redeem us from all ________________ (3 down)."
- Romans 12:16 "Do not be ____________ (4 down)"
- Psalm 19:12 "Declare me innocent from hidden ____________ (5 across)"
- Psalm 45:17 "I will __________ (8 across) your name to be remembered."
- Jn. 14:10 "I do not speak on my own _____________ (2 down)."
- Judges 15:15 "He found a fresh _______________ (6 down) of a donkey..."

								1	2	
						3				
			4		5					
	6									
7										
			8							

authority	haughty
cause	jawbone
daughter	law
faults	lawlessness

Day 66

Clue: This is how you spell the **multiples of ten:**

20 - **twenty**	70 - **seventy**
30 - **thirty**	80 - **eighty**
40 - **forty**	90 - **ninety**
50 - **fifty**	100 - **hundred**
60 - **sixty**	1000 - **thousand**

When writing checks, it is important to spell numbers correctly. For the first check (below), pay your tithe of $40 to *your church*.

001

Date__________________

Pay to the
order of____________________________________ $

____Dollars

Your Town Bank
Your town, USA 12345

For________________________ __________________________

1:234345456:78910443322"11

For the second check, you must pay $120 to *your parents* for room and board.

002

Date__________________

Pay to the
order of____________________________________ $

____Dollars

Your Town Bank
Your town, USA 12345

For________________________ __________________________

1:234345456:78910443322"11

For the third check, you are sending *your cousin* a Birthday check in the amount of $30.

003

Date__________________

Pay to the
order of____________________________________ $

____Dollars

Your Town Bank
Your town, USA 12345

For________________________ __________________________

1:234345456:78910443322"11

Clue: This is how you spell the **multiples of ten:**

20 - ____________ 70 - ____________
30 - ____________ 80 - ____________
40 - ____________ 90 - ____________
50 - ____________ 100 - ____________
60 - ____________ 1000 - ____________

For your first check, you just bought a car from *your best friend* for $4,000.

004

Date____________

Pay to the
order of______________________________ $ [ ]

______________________________Dollars

Your Town Bank
Your town, USA 12345

For____________ ____________

1:234345456:78910443322"11

For the second check, you must pay *your insurance company* $850 for your car insurance.

005

Date____________

Pay to the
order of______________________________ $ [ ]

______________________________Dollars

Your Town Bank
Your town, USA 12345

For____________ ____________

1:234345456:78910443322"11

For your third check, you must pay *Mastercard* $70 for the gasoline you charged for your car this month.

006

Date____________

Pay to the
order of______________________________ $ [ ]

______________________________Dollars

Your Town Bank
Your town, USA 12345

For____________ ____________

1:234345456:78910443322"11

Day 68

Clue: This is how you spell the **multiples of ten:**

20 -	______	70 -	______
30 -	______	80 -	______
40 -	______	90 -	______
50 -	______	100 -	______
60 -	______	1000 -	______

For your first check, you are going to send your favorite missionary a gift of $160.

007

Date______________

Pay to the
order of____ $ [ ]

____Dollars

Your Town Bank
Your town, USA 12345

For________________________ ________________________

1:234345456:78910443322"11

For your second check, you just bought Christmas presents at *Wal-Mart* worth $80.

008

Date______________

Pay to the
order of____ $ [ ]

____Dollars

Your Town Bank
Your town, USA 12345

For________________________ ________________________

1:234345456:78910443322"11

For the third check, you must pay *your phone company* $140 for this month's cell phone bill.

009

Date______________

Pay to the
order of____ $ [ ]

____Dollars

Your Town Bank
Your town, USA 12345

For________________________ ________________________

1:234345456:78910443322"11

Clue: This is how you spell the **multiples of ten:**

20 - ______________ 70 - ______________
30 - ______________ 80 - ______________
40 - ______________ 90 - ______________
50 - ______________ 100 - ______________
60 - ______________ 1000 - ______________

For your first check, it's time to pay *your local community college* for your first semester's tuition: $2,090.

010

Date______________

Pay to the order of________________________________ $

________________________________Dollars

Your Town Bank
Your town, USA 12345

For________________ ________________

1:234345456:78910443322"11

For the second check, you want to pay *your church* tithe again in the amount of $50.

011

Date______________

Pay to the order of________________________________ $

________________________________Dollars

Your Town Bank
Your town, USA 12345

For________________ ________________

1:234345456:78910443322"11

For your last check, you owe *your neighbor* $130, because he cut your grass weekly throughout the entire summer.

012

Date______________

Pay to the order of________________________________ $

________________________________Dollars

Your Town Bank
Your town, USA 12345

For________________ ________________

1:234345456:78910443322"11

Day 70 Review

Clue: The **long -o** sound in the ***middle*** of a word is usually spelled one of two ways:

- An ___ with a **silent** ____ on the end (as in *hope*).
- An ______ (as in *coat*).

If the word ***ends*** with a **long -o** sound, it is usually spelled with an -____ (as in *snow*). Occasionally it is spelled with an -__ (as in *go* and *no*) or an -____ (as in *toe*).

Clue: The spellings for the numbers, one to twelve, must be memorized. Several of them don't follow typical spelling rules:

1 - ________	**5** - ________	**9** - ________
2 - ________	**6** - ________	**10** - ________
3 - ________	**7** - ________	**11** - ________
4 - ________	**8** - ________	**12** - ________

Fill in the blanks using **long -o-** and **number words.**

coats	five	go	nose	snow	toes
cones	four	home	one	suppose	trombone
eight	froze	hope	piano		two

1. A ______________, which is a brass instrument, has a slide, while a ______________ has eighty-____________.

2. There are ___________ seasons, summer being the season in which we eat the most ice-cream __________, and winter being the season for wearing ____________.

3. Our _________ is in the _________ true God.

4. God gave us _________ feet, each with _________ __________.

5. My ___________ ____________ on my face during the ____________ storm.

6. ______ ye into all the world.

7. Do you ________________ Jesus will take us _________ soon?

Clue: The **long -e** sound in the ***middle*** of a word is usually spelled one of two ways:
- With and **-ee-** as in *feet,*
- With an **-ea-** as in *meat.*

Complete the definitions using **-ee-** words.

1. Shopping foray: ______________
2. The ages from 13-19: ______________
3. Not quite a crawl: ______________
4. A quick look: ______________
5. What a broom does: ______________
6. Profession: ______________
7. Mozzarella, cheddar, etc.: ______________
8. What a tire covers: ______________
9. What a wound will do: ______________
10. Covers a bed: ______________
11. Smooth, aerodynamic: ______________
12. Very smelly: ______________
13. Wild plants: ______________
14. Hurrah! ______________
15. The arm of a shirt: ______________

bleed
career
cheer
cheese
creep
peep
reek
sheet
sleek
sleeve
spree
sweep
teen
weeds
wheel

Day 72

Clue: The **long -e** sound in the ***middle*** of a word is usually spelled one of two ways:
- With and _______ as in *feet,*
- With an ________ as in *meat.*

Complete the following Scriptures with **-ee-** words. One is used twice.

deep	greet	meek	weeping
feet	heed	seeds	
flee	indeed	sheep	
free	keep	sleep	

1. Luke 7:38 "______________, she began to wet his _________ with her tears and wiped them with the hair of her head."
2. James 4:7 "Resist the devil, and he will _________ from you."
3. John 8:36 "If the Son sets you _________, you will be _________ ________________."
4. 3 John 15 "The friends _____________ you."
5. Matthew 13:8 "Other ______________ fell on good soil..."
6. Mark 13:33 "Take ___________, __________ awake."
7. John 10:3 "He calls His own _____________ by name."
8. Genesis 2:21 "The LORD God caused a ____________ _____________ to fall upon the man..."
9. Matthew 5:5 "Blessed are the _____________..."

Clue: The **long -e** sound in the ***middle*** of a word is usually spelled one of two ways:
- With and ________ as in *feet*,
- With an _________ as in *meat*.

Complete the clues, then find the **-ee-** words in the puzzle.

1. Group of ships: ______________
2. Consent to: _______________
3. Road: _______________
4. Core belief: ______________
5. Necessity:_____________
6. Below 32 ⊠: ______________
7. Bow down: ____________
8. Oak, maple: _________________
9. Seven days: ________________
10. Horn sound: ____________
11. Blue and yellow: ___________
12. Cow meat: _______________

q	w	e	r	t	y	k	u	i	o	p	a
s	n	e	e	d	d	n	f	g	h	j	t
k	l	z	x	c	v	e	b	b	m	e	n
f	m	q	w	e	r	e	t	y	e	u	i
l	o	d	p	a	s	l	d	r	e	f	g
e	h	j	e	b	k	l	t	z	r	x	c
e	v	b	n	e	m	s	q	w	g	e	b
t	e	z	e	e	r	f	r	r	a	t	e
y	w	y	u	p	i	c	e	o	p	a	e
a	e	s	d	f	g	e	h	j	k	l	f
z	e	x	c	v	n	b	n	m	q	w	e
r	k	t	y	u	i	o	t	r	e	e	a

agree	fleet	need
beef	freeze	street
beep	green	tree
creed	kneel	week

Day 74

> **Clue:** The **long -e** sound in the ***middle*** of a word is usually spelled one of two ways:
> - With and ________ as in *feet*,
> - With an ________ as in *meat*.

Complete the definitions with **-ee-** words.

1. Say hello: ______________
2. Freezing rain: ______________
3. Wanting it all for yourself: ______________
4. Horse: ______________
5. Grecian language: ______________
6. Coral barrier: ______________
7. Cry: ______________
8. Molars, cuspids, etc.: ______________
9. Touch: ______________
10. Sugary: ______________
11. Mock: ______________
12. Get acquainted: ______________
13. The number 3: ______________
14. Quickness: ______________
15. Give food to: ______________
16. Change direction: ______________

feed
feel
greed
Greek
greet
jeer
meet
reef
sleet
speed
steed
sweet
teeth
three
veer
weep

Clue: The **long -e** sound in the ***middle*** of a word is usually spelled one of two ways:
- With and ________ as in *feet*,
- With an ________ as in *meat*.

Complete the following definitions with **-ea-** words.

1. To deceive: ____________________
2. Special food or outing: ______________
3. On a necklace: _____________
4. Hot vapor: _______________
5. Behind: _____________
6. Eye moisture: ______________
7. Inexpensive: ________________
8. Turquoise: ___________
9. Lima, wax, string, etc.: _______________
10. To beg: _______________
11. Not kind: _____________
12. Orderly: _______________
13. Without fat: ______________
14. Young cow meat: ______________
15. Not hazy: ____________________

bead
bean
cheap
cheat
clear
lean
mean
neat
plead
rear
steam
teal
tear
treat
veal

Day 76

Clue: The **long -e** sound in the ***middle*** of a word is usually spelled one of two ways: ▪ With and ________ as in *feet,* ▪ With an _________ as in *meat.*

Complete the following Scriptures with **-ea-** words.

beast	lead	speak
clean	leaf	streams
ear	near	teach
eat	peace	tears
fear	reaping	wheat
hear	season	

1. 1 Samuel 6:13 "The people...were __________ their ___________ harvest."

2. Psalm 1:3 "He is like a tree planted by ___________ of water that yields fruit in its ______________, and its ____________ does not wither."

3. Ps. 25:5 "___________ me in your truth and _____________me."

4. Psalm 19:9 "The ___________ of the LORD is ___________..."

5. Rev. 13:15 "...The image of the ______________ might even ________________."

6. Psalm 39:12 "___________ my prayer, O LORD, and give ________ to my cry; hold not your __________ at my ____________!"

7. Hebrews 10:22 "Let us draw __________ with a true heart..."

8. 2 Thessalonians 3:10 "If anyone is not willing to work, let him not __________."

Clue: The **long -e** sound in the ***middle*** of a word is usually spelled one of two ways:

- With and ________ as in *feet*,
- With an _________ as in *meat*.

Complete the clues with **-ea-** words, then complete the puzzle.

Across

2. To make well: ____________
6. Brook: ____________
8. Tipped weapon: ____________
9. Hot vapor: ____________
10. Bird mouth: ____________
12. Lack strength: ____________
13. Verbalize: ____________
14. Transparently: ____________

Down

1. Coordinated groups: ________
3. Listen: ____________
4. Lightening flash: ____________
5. Light ray: ____________
7. Escape crack: ____________
11. Simple: ____________

							1				
						2					3
			4		5						
		6							7		
							8				
	9										
						10	11				
12											
							13				
	14										

beak	speak
beam	spear
clearly	steam
easy	streak
heal	stream
hear	teams
leak	weak

Day 78

Clue: The **long -e** sound in the ***middle*** of a word is usually spelled one of two ways:
- With and ________ as in *feet*,
- With an ________ as in *meat*.

Complete the definitions with **-ea-** words.

1. To hit repeatedly: ______________
2. Hotness: ___________
3. Animal flesh:_____________
4. Breakfast, lunch, dinner: ___________
5. Not west: ____________
6. Do or say again: _____________
7. Supports a structure: _______________
8. Fat part of milk: _____________
9. Sleeping vision: ______________
10. Gather grain: ____________
11. Bundle of paper: ___________
12. Stitched sides: ______________
13. Pile: ___________
14. Jump: ___________
15. Darling: _____________

beam
beat
cream
dear
dream
east
glean
heap
heat
leap
meal
meat
ream
repeat
seam

Clue: The **long -e** sound in the ***middle*** of a word is usually spelled one of two ways:

- With and ________ as in *feet*,
- With an ________ as in *meat*.

Homophones are pairs of words that sound the same, but mean something different. Fill in the blanks with the correct homophones.

1. Dog's insect: ____________
2. Run away: ____________

3. Get acquainted: ____________
4. Animal flesh: ____________

5. Hit repeatedly: ____________
6. Vegetable: ____________

7. Decipher writing: ____________
8. Water plant: ____________

9. Mountain top: ____________
10. Quick glimpse: ____________

11. Seven days: ____________
12. Lack strength: ____________

13. Back of foot: ____________
14. To make well: ____________

15. Genuine: ____________
16. Part of fishing rod: ____________

17. Metal: ____________
18. Take another's belongings: ____________

19. Ocean: ____________
20. Look: ____________

beat
beet
flea
flee
heal
heel
meat
meet
peak
peek
read
reed
real
reel
sea
see
steal
steel
weak
week

Day 80 Review

Clue: How do you keep the words *was, want,* and *what* straight? • ______is the past tense of the word *is*. The "uh" sound is spelled with an __, and there is no -__-. It is a short word, just like all of the "be" verbs. • ________means *desire*. It does not have an -__, nor an apostrophe. Remember: You ________ always have what you________. • ________is one of the "5 w's" (who, _______, where, when, and why). All "5 w's" begin with "____".
Clue: The **short -o-** sound (as in *law*) is often spelled one of two ways. These must be memorized. ▪ With an ______ (as in *author*) ▪ With an ______ (as in *fawn*)
Clue: The **-ou- sound** (as in the word '*out*') is usually spelled one of two ways. These spellings must be memorized: • With an _____ as in **south**. • With an _____ as in **cow**.

Circle the misspelled words in the sentences below, then spell the words correctly on the lines following.

1. It wuz early daun when the hownd fownd the sawsage thauing on the table. _________ ___________ _____________ _____________ _________________ _______________

2. He wunted that meat! ______________

3. He pushed it with his pau onto the floor and ate the rau meat quickly before he got cawght. _________ _________ ___________________

4. We sau wut he wuz doing, tawght him a lesson he wouldn't forget, and put him owt of the howse. ____________ ____________ __________ ________________ _________ ______________

5. He houled, but we were undawnted by the nawty dog. _______________ ________________ ______________

Lesson 81

Clue: The **long -u-** sound can be spelled a number of ways, including:

- **-oo-** (as in *zoo*)
- **-u-silent-e** (as in *tune*)
- **-ew** (as in *new*)
- **-ue** (as in *clue*)

Complete the definitions with **-oo-** words.

1. Used to weave: ________________
2. Faint: _____________
3. Attitude: _________________
4. Place for learning: __________________
5. Almost cold: _______________
6. To aim and fire: ________________
7. Chicken house: ______________
8. Underground plant part: _____________
9. Earth's satellite: ______________
10. 12:00 PM: _______________
11. Eating utensil: ________________
12. A thread circle: _____________
13. Bend over: ______________
14. House part: _____________
15. Evidence: _____________

cool
coop
loom
loop
mood
moon
noon
proof
room
root
school
shoot
spoon
stoop
swoon

Lesson 82

Clue: The **long -u-** sound can be spelled a number of ways, including:

- _____ (as in *zoo*)
- __________ (as in *tune*)
- _____ (as in *new*)
- _____ (as in *clue*)

Complete the Scriptures with **-oo-** words.

choose	gloom	room	tool
food	noonday	roots	wool
fool	roof	soon	

1. Psalm 136:25 "It is He who gives _________ to all flesh..."
2. Mark 2:4 "They removed the ___________ above him..."
3. Psalm 14:1 "The _________ says in his heart, 'There is no God.'"
4. 1 Kings 6:7 "...Nor any ________ of iron was heard in the temple..."
5. Revelation 2:20 "Surely I am coming __________."
6. Revelation 1:14 "The hairs of His head were white like __________."
7. Luke 2:7 "There was no ________ for them in the inn."
8. Isaiah 58:10 "...Your _________ shall be as the _____________."
9. Joshua 24:15 "_____________this day whom you will serve."
10. Mark 11:20 "...The fig tree withered away to its ___________."

Lesson 83

Clue: The **long -u-** sound can be spelled a number of ways, including:

- ______ (as in *zoo*)
- ____________ (as in *tune*)
- ______ (as in *new*)
- ______ (as in *clue*)

Complete the clues with **-oo-** , then find them in the puzzle.

1. Animal place: __________
2. Incubate eggs: __________
3. Cow sound: __________
4. Chase away: __________
5. Silly: __________
6. Distant: __________
7. Swimming place: __________
8. Thread keeper: __________
9. Sweeper: __________
10. Wilt: __________
11. Circular frame: __________
12. Soldiers: __________
13. Footwear: __________
14. In your mouth: __________
15. Not bride: __________
16. Masked animal: __________

c	q	w	e	r	b	r	o	o	d	t	y
u	o	i	o	d	r	o	o	p	o	o	h
p	o	o	a	s	o	d	f	g	h	j	k
l	z	z	n	o	o	c	c	a	r	m	m
q	a	z	w	l	m	s	x	s	e	d	o
s	c	r	y	f	o	v	h	p	t	g	o
p	b	y	f	h	n	o	m	o	u	j	m
o	i	k	o	l	o	p	p	o	z	a	q
o	b	t	o	o	t	h	x	r	o	s	w
l	c	o	g	d	e	v	f	t	r	r	b
g	t	n	o	h	y	m	j	u	k	i	g
o	l	p	m	t	n	b	a	l	o	o	f

aloof	droop	moo	spool
boot	goofy	pool	tooth
brood	groom	raccoon	troops
broom	hoop	shoo	zoo

Lesson 84

Clue: The **long -u-** sound can be spelled a number of ways, including:
- _____ (as in *zoo*)
- __________ (as in *tune*)
- _____ (as in *new*)
- _____ (as in *clue*)

Complete the following definitions with **-u-silent-e** words.

1. A square prism: ____________
2. Discourteous: ____________
3. A dandy: ____________
4. The sixth month: ____________
5. Showy feathers: ____________
6. Dried plum: ____________
7. Sand hill: ____________
8. Sing: ____________
9. Beast: ____________
10. Slide: ____________
11. Pretty, adorable: ____________
12. Fork, spoon, knife: ____________
13. Begin again: ____________
14. To involve: ____________
15. To blame: ____________
16. Silent: ____________
17. Mix up: ____________

accuse
brute
chute
confuse
cube
cute
dude
dune
include
June
mute
plume
prune
rude
resume
tune
utensil

Lesson 85

Clue: The **long -u-** sound can be spelled a number of ways, including:

- _____ (as in *zoo*)
- __________ (as in *tune*)
- _____ (as in *new*)
- _____ (as in *clue*)

Complete the following Scriptures with **-u-silent-e** words.

accuser	prunes	rule
disputed	refuge	ruler
lukewarm	refuse	
mule	rude	

1. 1 Corinthians 13:5 "Love is not ___________."
2. 2 Samuel 18:9 "Absalom was riding on his __________."
3. Colossians 3:15 "Let the peace of Christ __________ in your hearts..."
4. Proverb 29:26 "Many seek the face of a ____________..."
5. Mark 9:34 "...They had ____________ among themselves..."
6. Acts 25:11 "__________ not to die."
7. John 15:2 "Every branch that does not bear fruit he ____________..."
8. Revelation 3:16 "Because you are _______________, I will spit you out..."
9. Psalm 46:1 "God is our ___________ and strength..."
10. Revelation 12:10 "For the _____________ of our brothers has been thrown down..."

Lesson 86

Clue: The **long -u-** sound can be spelled a number of ways, including:

- _____ (as in *zoo*)
- ___________ (as in *tune*)
- _____ (as in *new*)
- _____ (as in *clue*)

Complete the following definitions with **-ew** words.

1. Not too many: ____________
2. Chomp: ____________
3. Israeli: ____________
4. Kitten sound: ____________
5. Past tense of draw: ____________
6. Recently made: ____________
7. Church bench: ____________
8. Past tense of fly: ____________
9. Morning condensation: ____________
10. Past tense of know: ____________
11. Soup: ____________
12. Got bigger: ____________
13. Concoct: ____________
14. Past tense of blow: ____________
15. Ship's men: ____________

blew
brew
chew
crew
dew
drew
few
flew
grew
Jew
knew
mew
new
pew
stew

Lesson 87

Clue: The **long -u-** sound can be spelled a number of ways, including:

- _____ (as in *zoo*)
- ___________ (as in *tune*)
- _____ (as in *new*)
- _____ (as in *clue*)

Complete the following definitions with **-ue** words.

1. Adhesive: ____________
2. Permeate: ____________
3. A primary color: ____________
4. Accurate: ____________
5. Hint: ___________
6. Color or shade: ____________
7. Owed now: ____________
8. Girl's name: ____________
9. Signal: ____________
10. Speaks or writes easily: ____________
11. Accumulate regularly: ____________
12. Take place as a result: ____________

accrue
blue
clue
cue
due
ensue
fluent
glue
hue
imbue
Sue
true

Lesson 88

Clue: The **long -u-** sound can be spelled a number of ways, including:

- _____ (as in *zoo*)
- ___________ (as in *tune*)
- _____ (as in *new*)
- _____ (as in *clue*)

Complete the following Scriptures with **-ue** and **-ew** words.

blew	few	new
blue	grew	stew
chew	Jews	sue
dew	knew	true

1. Deuteronomy 14:8 "The pig...does not ________ the cud..."
2. Acts 27:13 "...The south wind _________ gently..."
3. Proverb 19:12 "...His favor is like _______ on the grass."
4. Numbers 4:7 "...They shall spread a cloth of _________..."
5. Mt. 9:37 "The harvest is plentiful, but the laborers are ______."
6. John 19:19 "Jesus of Nazareth, the King of the __________."
7. Revelation 21:5 "Behold, I am making all things ________."
8. 2 Cor. 5:21 "He made Him to be sin who ________ no sin..."
9. Matthew 5:40 "If anyone would ________ you...let him have your cloak as well."
10. Luke 2:40 And Jesus __________ in wisdom..."
11. Genesis 25:30 "Let me eat some of that red _________..."
12. Jeremiah 10:10 "The LORD is the __________ God."

Lesson 89

Clue: The **long -u-** sound can be spelled a number of ways, including:

- _____ (as in *zoo*)
- ___________ (as in *tune*)
- _____ (as in *new*)
- _____ (as in *clue*)

Complete the following clues, and then the puzzle, with **-ew** and **-ue** words.

Across

4. Believable: ____________
5. Eat: _________
7. Ship's men: ___________
8. Pipe, chimney: __________
9. Lawsuit: __________
11. Illustrated: _________
12. Israeli: _________

Down

1. Thick soup: ___________
2. Owed: __________
3. Accumulate: ____________
6. Color: __________
7. Hint: ___________
8. Soared: __________
10. Got bigger: ___________

						1		2			
			3			4					
			5								
										6	
	7							8			
9						10					
					11						
				12							

accrue	crew	flue	sue
blue	drew	grew	true
chew	due	Jew	
clue	flew	stew	

Lesson 90 Review

Clue:

- When you are adding a suffix (ending) to a word that **ends in "___"**, you should *change the "____" to an "____", then add the__________.*
- When you are adding a suffix (ending) to a word that **ends in a vowel plus "y"**, *do not* __________ *the "___" to an "__"*, or you'll have too many vowels in a row.
- When you are adding the **suffix -ing** to a word ending in -y, *do not* __________ *the "___" to an "____"*, or you'll have two i's in a row.

Clue: The **short -o-** sound (as in *law*) is often spelled one of two ways. These must be memorized.

- With an ______ (as in *author*)
- With an ______ (as in *fawn*)

Clue: The **-oi-** sound is spelled one of two ways. These spellings must be memorized.

- When a word ______ in the sound, it is spelled -____ (as in **boy**)...
- When the sound is in the _________ of a word, it is *usually* spelled with an -___- (as in **coin**).

Circle the misspelled words in the sentences below, then spell them correctly on the lines following.

1. The embarrassed boi's changing voyce squauked as he tryed to sing for the ladys of the committee. ____________ ________________ ______________ _____________ ______________

2. The rawcous crowd cheered noysily under the auning as the outfielder cawght the ball in the hot Awgust sun. ________________ ____________ ____________ ___________ ___________

3. In many citys crime has spoyled the secure feeling of people as they sawnter past auful degradation every day. ______________ _____________ _____________ ______________

4. His dawter turned on the fawcet so she could boyl water for the dumplings and pastrys she was cooking for her family's enjoiment. _____________ ______________ ___________ ______________ _________________

Clue: The **long-i-** sound can be spelled a number of different ways, including the following:

- With an **-i -silent -e** (as in *kite*)
- With a **-y** (as in *try*) if the word *ends* in the long -i- sound
- With an **-ight** if the word ends with a **long -i** sound **plus -t** (as in *light*). The **-gh** is silent.

Spell the **-ight** words correctly in the chart below.

br"ite"	f"ite"
r"ite"	t"ite"
l"ite"	s"ite"

Use the correctly-spelled words above in the sentences below.

1. Who forgot to turn off the ____________?

2. Never look directly at an eclipse if you want to protect your ____________.

3. We should never ____________. Instead we should learn to turn the other cheek.

4. When the sun is too ____________, I wear sunglasses.

5. "Many sons had Father Abraham. I am one of them, and so are you, so let's just praise the Lord. ____________ foot, left foot..."

6. If your pants are too ____________, you can loosen your belt a notch.

Circle the misspelled words in the sentences below and write them correctly on the lines.

7. It is not rite for a Christian to fite. ____________ ____________
8. The star shown forth with a brite lite.____________ ____________
9. In a tite schedule, never lose site of Jesus.____________ ____________

Day 92

Clue: The **long-i-** sound can be spelled a number of different ways, including the following:

- With an -______________ (as in *kite*)
- With a -_________ (as in *try*) if the word ________ in the long -i- sound
- With an -_________ if the word ends with a **long -i** sound **plus -t** (as in *light*). The -_________ is silent.

Spell the **-ight** words correctly in the chart below.

bl"ite"	fl"ite"
fr"ite"	pl"ite"
m"ite"	n"ite"

Use the correctly-spelled words above in the sentences below.

1. Our hearts should be moved to compassion by the ____________ of the homeless.
2. You should love the Lord with all your __________________.
3. Jesus will return like a thief in the __________________.
4. The crops were ruined by a particularly ravaging ______________.
5. With the new security measures, you must arrive at the airport two hours before your ______________.
6. You should have seen the look of ____________________ on his face when we jumped out at him from behind the door!

Circle the misspelled words in the sentences below and write them correctly on the lines.

7. The blite in the corn put the farmer in a real plite.
8. I mite prefer to drive if I can't get an earlier flite.
9. The sounds in the nite made Monica shake with frite.

____________________ ____________________

____________________ ____________________

____________________ ____________________

Clue: The **long-i-** sound can be spelled a number of different ways, including the following:

- With an -_____________ (as in *kite*)
- With a -_________ (as in *try*) if the word ________ in the long -i- sound
- With an -_________ if the word ends with a **long -i** sound **plus -t** (as in *light*). The -_________ is silent.

Find 10 **-ight** words in the word search puzzle below. Use the words to fill in the blanks in the sentences below.

1. The coach turned into a pumpkin at __________________.
2. If it isn't wrong, it's ___________________.
3. Chris replaced the ____________________ in the lamp.
4. What a __________________ God we serve.
5. The sun was too ___________________ without my sunglasses.
6. What a __________________ it was to see a rainbow over the Grand Canyon!
7. Christians __________ the Enemy with the Sword of the Spirit.
8. That parking spot was too _____________ to park our big van.
9. I enjoyed the plane _______________ over the Grand Canyon.
10. Our souls are ___________________ by sin.

r	a	w	q	y	o	p	a	s	d	f	g	b
h	i	j	k	l	z	m	x	c	v	b	n	l
m	q	g	w	e	s	i	g	h	t	r	t	u
y	u	i	h	o	p	a	s	d	f	g	h	b
c	x	m	z	t	l	k	j	f	i	g	h	t
v	b	i	i	n	m	q	w	l	e	r	t	h
y	u	g	i	d	o	p	a	i	s	d	f	g
g	h	h	j	k	n	l	z	g	x	c	v	i
b	n	t	m	b	l	i	g	h	t	e	d	l
q	w	y	e	r	r	t	g	t	y	u	i	o
p	a	s	d	i	f	g	h	h	j	k	l	z
x	c	v	b	g	n	m	q	g	t	w	e	r
t	y	u	i	h	o	o	p	i	a	s	d	f
f	g	h	j	t	k	l	z	t	x	c	v	b

bright, blighted, fight, flight, lightbulb, mighty, midnight, right, sight, tight

Day 94

Clue: The **long-i-** sound can be spelled a number of different ways, including the following:

- With an -_____________ (as in *kite*)
- With a -________ (as in *try*) if the word ________ in the long -i- sound
- With an -_________ if the word ends with a **long -i** sound **plus -t** (as in *light*). The -_________ is silent.

Complete the puzzle with **-ight** words using the clues below.

Across

1. Powerful: _______________
2. _____________D. Eisenhower
5. Screws in socket: __________
8. Plane ride: _____________
9. Squeezed: _______________
10. Disease: _______________

Down

1. 12:00 AM: ______________
3. Ability to see: _____________
4. Difficulty: _____________
6. Blindingly: ______________
7. Not left: ____________
8. Bad scare: ______________

(Answers in alphabetic order: blight, brightly, Dwight, flight, fright, light bulb, midnight, mighty, plight, right, sight, tight.)

Clue: The **long-i-** sound can be spelled a number of different ways, including the following:

- With an -______________ (as in *kite*)
- With a -_________ (as in *try*) if the word ________ in the long -i- sound
- With an -_________ if the word ends with a **long -i** sound **plus -t** (as in *light*). The -_________ is silent.

Complete the following definitions with **-i-silent-e** words.

1. Miss the ball in baseball: ________________
2. Fine cable: ______________
3. Number 5: ______________
4. Ten cents: ______________
5. Long walk: ______________
6. Sparkle: ________________
7. Bell: _______________
8. Not husband: _____________
9. Flames: ______________
10. Small rodents: _______________
11. Incline: _______________
12. Frozen water: _____________
13. Clinging plant: ______________
14. Living: _______________
15. Soaring toy on a string: _____________

alive
chime
dime
fire
five
hike
ice
kite
mice
shine
slide
strike
vine
wife
wire

Day 96

> **Clue:** The **long-i-** sound can be spelled a number of different ways, including the following:
> - With an -______________ (as in *kite*)
> - With a -_________ (as in *try*) if the word ________ in the long -i- sound
> - With an -_________ if the word ends with a **long -i** sound **plus -t** (as in *light*). The -_________ is silent.

Complete the Scriptures with **-i-silent-e** words. One is used twice.

abide	life	white
Bride	like	wife
defile	pride	wise
fire	time	
hide	vine	

1. Psalm 27:9 "__________ not your face from me."

2. 1 John 2:16 "...The ________ of ________ is not of the Father..."

3. Matthew 15:20 "To eat with unwashed hands does not ____________ anyone."

4. John 15:4 "____________ in me, and I in you."

5. Ephesians 5:15-16 "Be __________, making the best use of the ____________..."

6. Revelation 19:12 "His eyes are __________ a flame of ________."

7. Revelation 21:9 "I will show you the ____________, the ________ of the Lamb."

8. John 15:1 "I am the true __________."

9. Isaiah 1:18 "Though your sins are __________ scarlet, they shall be _____________ as snow."

Clue: The **long-i-** sound can be spelled a number of different ways, including the following:

- With an -_______________ (as in *kite*)
- With a -__________ (as in *try*) if the word ________ in the long -i- sound
- With an -__________ if the word ends with a **long -i** sound **plus -t** (as in *light*). The -__________ is silent.

Complete the clues and puzzle with **-i-silent-e** words.

Across

1. Pig: ________________
4. Slope: ______________
6. Only tell you: ____________
7. Frozen water: __________
8. Tempt: ___________
9. Cutter: _____________

Down

1. Ten pins down: _______________
2. Perfect: _________________
3. Egypt river: ____________
5. Herb: _____________
6. To cage: ______________

							1				
									2		3
			4		5						
	6								7		
8											
9											

chive	ice	refine
confide	incline	strike
confine	knife	swine
entice	Nile	

Day 98

Clue: The **long-i-** sound can be spelled a number of different ways, including the following:

- With an -_______________ (as in *kite*)
- With a -_________ (as in *try*) if the word ________ in the long –i- sound
- With an -_________ if the word ends with a **long -i** sound **plus -t** (as in *light*). The -_________ is silent.

Complete the definitions with **-i-silent-e** words.

1. Tempt with money: _______________
2. Grain: _______________
3. To be enough: _______________
4. Two times: _______________
5. Extensive: _______________
6. Backbone: _______________
7. Cost: _______________
8. Heap: _______________
9. Citrus fruit: _______________
10. Grin: _______________
11. People group: _______________
12. Scum: _______________
13. Number 9: _______________
14. Covers a wheel: _______________
15. Distance of 5,280 feet: _______________

bribe
lime
mile
nine
pile
price
rice
slime
smile
spine
suffice
tire
tribe
twice
wide

Clue: The **long-i-** sound can be spelled a number of different ways, including the following:

- With an -__________ (as in *kite*)
- With a -________ (as in *try*) if the word _______ in the long -i- sound
- With an -________ if the word ends with a **long -i** sound **plus -t** (as in *light*). The -________ is silent.

Complete the sentences with **-i-silent-e** words, or words ending in **-y.**

bike	lime	pipe	slice	wife
bite	miles	price	smiles	wise
fine	Nile	pry	surprise	
grime	nine	shine	try	
kite	pine	side	why	

1. My __________ tried one _________ from my __________ of key __________ pie.
2. Stephen has a face that will ___________ right through the __________ when he ______________.
3. __________ should we __________ to _____________ Dwayne with a ____________ tie when he seldom wears them?
4. Chris wanted to ________ the nails from the __________ boards, so he could build a half-__________ for his __________.
5. The __________ River runs for many __________ through the Egyptian country__________.
6. Ben was __________ to check the __________ before paying _________ dollars for the __________.

Day 100 Review

Clue:

- When you are adding a suffix (ending) to a word that **ends in "____"**, you should *change the "____" to an "____", then add the*____________.
- When you are adding a suffix (ending) to a word that **ends in a vowel plus "y"**, *do not* ____________ *the "___" to an "__"*, or you'll have too many vowels in a row.
- When you are adding the **suffix -ing** to a word ending in -y, *do not* ____________ *the "___" to an "____"*, or you'll have two i's in a row.

Clue: This is how you spell the **multiples of ten:**

20 - ________________	70 - ________________
30 - ________________	80 - ________________
40 - ________________	90 - ________________
50 - ________________	100 - ________________
60 - ________________	1000 - ________________

Add the suffix **-ed** to the following words:

hop____________	smile____________	tan____________	sin____________
jump____________	camp____________	flip____________	part____________
skip____________	pin____________	hate____________	beg____________

Write a tithe check for $140 to *your church*.

015

Date____________________

Pay to the
order of____ $ [ ]

____Dollars

Your Town Bank
Your town, USA 12345

For______________________ ______________________

1:234345456:78910443322"11

Write a $280 check to *your parents* for 2 months' room and board.

016

Date____________________

Pay to the
order of____ $ [ ]

____Dollars

Your Town Bank
Your town, USA 12345

For______________________ ______________________

1:234345456:78910443322"11

Clue: The following words are tricky and should be memorized.

- The word ***why*** has a silent **-h-**
- ***Does*** is the verb ***do*** with an **-es** on the end
- ***Only*** has a **long-o** sound
- ***Who*** has a silent **w-**. It rhymes with *two* (which also has a silent -w-)

Use the words **why, does, only,** and **who** in the sentences below.

1. ____________ __________ he always have to be first?
2. Baby Angelina had ___________ one tooth.
3. I wonder _________ was the first person to taste frog legs.
4. __________ _________ this pair of socks belong to?
5. I know _________ Monica eats meatloaf _________ if it is covered with ketchup.
6. ___________ anyone have a pair of scissors?
7. He ___________!
8. There is ___________ one true God.
9. __________ is like our God?
10. Michael may have __________ one cookie.

Day 102

Clue: The following words are tricky and should be memorized.

- The word ***why*** has a silent -______-
- ***Does*** is the verb _________ with an -_____ on the end
- ***Only*** has a __________ sound
- ***Who*** has a silent _____. It rhymes with ______ (which also has a silent -___-)

Use the words **why, does, only,** and **who** in the sentences below.

1. __________ won't anyone help her?
2. __________ anyone know _________ that is?
3. There are _____________ twenty-four hours in a day.
4. Christy ___________ not like going to the dentist.
5. I heard of a man ___________ will live in a suspended glass box, drinking ___________ water, for 44 days.
6. __________ would anyone do such a crazy thing?
7. Josh __________ fifty sit-ups every morning.
8. __________ ____________ ice float?
9. I ___________ want a dog _________ doesn't shed.
10. _________ can explain the reason __________.

Clue: The following words are tricky and should be memorized.

- The word ***why*** has a silent -_____-
- ***Does*** is the verb ________ with an -____ on the end
- ***Only*** has a _________ sound
- ***Who*** has a silent ____. It rhymes with _____ (which also has a silent -__-)

Use the words **why, does, only,** and **who** in the sentences below.

1. Rebecca _________ like broccoli and Stephen ________ not.
2. Israel wanted _________ three peas on his plate.
3. _________ would like more cabbage?
4. Tell me _________ you won't have seconds on asparagus.
5. __________ the thought of zucchini make you ill?
6. I know _______ you want more corn-on-the-cob.
7. Ben ________ likes onions and garlic.
8. Kyle will eat lima beans _________ if they're smothered in butter.
9. __________ named the cauliflower?
10. _________ did Adam call it an eggplant?

Day 104

Clue: The following words are tricky and should be memorized.

- The word ***why*** has a silent -______-
- ***Does*** is the verb _________ with an -_____ on the end
- ***Only*** has a __________ sound
- ***Who*** has a silent _____. It rhymes with ______ (which also has a silent -___-)

Use the words **why, does, only,** and **who** in the sentences below.

1. ____________ ____________ the average person spend so much time on hobbies?
2. Not ____________ ___________ the average person spend time, but also money on hobbies.
3. __________ enjoys knitting?
4. ___________ anyone know ___________ I can hire to care for my gardens?
5. There's a reason _________ Joyce collects dryer lint.
6. I know a guy __________ carves ballpoint pens out of antlers.
7. ____________ Sue really make homemade soap?
8. Scott _____________ collects rolling pins.
9. ___________ Chris collect business cards?
10. Alan really ___________ like ___________ tuba music.

Clue: The following words are tricky and should be memorized.

- The word ***why*** has a silent -_____-
- ***Does*** is the verb ________ with an -____ on the end
- ***Only*** has a _________ sound
- ***Who*** has a silent ____. It rhymes with _____ (which also has a silent -__-)

Use the words **why, does, only,** and **who** in the sentences below.

1. Michael's car _________ _________ 130 miles per hour tops.
2. ________ ________ Dwayne's car always break down.
3. Chris has a friend _______ owns an Audi.
4. __________ an Audi go faster than a Mustang?
5. _________ will race against Aaron's Acura?
6. ________ won't Peter enter his BMW in the race?
7. Jonathan's car _________ accelerate faster than Dave's.
8. Caleb can __________ race his Camaro on Saturday.
9. Steve will _________ raise his truck if he has to.
10. _______ would anyone ________ has any sense enter a race?

Day 106

Clue: It is important to spell correctly when addressing envelopes. Remember the following rules:

- The **return address** (*your* address) goes in the **upper left-hand corner.**
- All Names, Streets, Towns, and States are capitalized.
- **Abbreviations** (except state abbreviations) are punctuated with a **period (.).**

(A chart of the state abbreviations is found on page 153 of the appendix.)

1. Address this envelope *from you* to *your grandparents.*

____
____
____

____
____
____

2. Address this envelope *from you* to *a friend.*

____
____
____

____
____
____

3. Address this envelope *from you* to *someone you know out-of-state.*

____
____
____

____
____
____

Clue: It is important to spell correctly when addressing envelopes. Remember the following rules:

- The ______________ (*your* address) goes in the **upper** _____________ **corner.**
- All ___ames, ____treets, ____owns, and ___tates are _____________.
- **Abbreviations** (except state abbreviations) are punctuated with a **period (__).**

(A chart of the state abbreviations is found on page 153 of the appendix.)

1. Address this envelope *from you* to *another friend.*

____
____
____

____
____
____

2. Address this envelope *from you* to *a cousin.*

____
____
____

____
____
____

3. Address this envelope *from you* to *your church.*

____
____
____

____
____
____

Day 108

Clue: It is important to spell correctly when addressing envelopes. Remember the following rules:

- The ______________ (*your* address) goes in the **upper** ____________ **corner.**
- All ___ames, ____treets, ____owns, and ___tates are ______________.
- **Abbreviations** (except state abbreviations) are punctuated with a **period (__).**

(A chart of the state abbreviations is found on page 153 of the appendix.)

1. Address this envelope *from you* to *a missionary.*

____
____
____

____
____
____

2. Address this envelope *from you* to *your electric company.*

____
____
____

____
____
____

3. Address this envelope *from you* to *your parents* (Yup, same address).

____
____
____

____
____
____

Clue: It is important to spell correctly when addressing envelopes. Remember the following rules:

- The _______________ (*your* address) goes in the **upper** ______________ **corner.**
- All ___ames, ____treets, ____owns, and ___tates are ______________.
- **Abbreviations** (except state abbreviations) are punctuated with a **period (__).**

(A chart of the state abbreviations is found on page 153 of the appendix.)

1. Address this envelope *from you* to *another cousin.*

2. Address this envelope *from you* to *someone else out-of-state.*

3. Address this envelope *from you* to *a neighbor.*

Day 110 Review

Clue: The **long -e** sound in the ***middle*** of a word is usually spelled one of two ways: ▪ With and ________ as in *feet*, ▪ With an _________ as in *meat*.
Clue: The **long -o** sound in the ***middle*** of a word is usually spelled one of two ways: • An ___ with a **silent** _____ on the end (as in *hope*). • An ______ (as in *coat*). If the word ***ends*** with a **long -o** sound, it is usually spelled with an -____ (as in *snow*). Occasionally it is spelled with an -__ (as in *go* and *no*) or an -____ (as in *toe*).

Complete the sentences with **long-o** and **long-e** words. One word is used twice.

1. (Hoam),___________ (swete)___________ (hoam)_________ is a popular saying.

2. On our farm, we (gro)___________ (benes)___________, (pees)_____________, and (otes)___________.

3. The (shepe)___________ in the pasture wore long, woolen (cotes)____________ as the (sno)__________ fell throughout the (weke)_____________.

4. The (steme)___________ (bote)___________ chugged swiftly through the Mediterranean (See)___________.

5. Could you (pleez)___________ answer the (phoan)___________.

beans	oats	sheep
boat	peas	snow
coats	phone	steam
grow	please	sweet
home	Sea	week

Clue: When a word ends in a syllable that sounds like...

- "**-iss,**" it is usually spelled **-ous** (as in *jealous*).
- "**-shiss,**" it is usually spelled **-cious** (as in *precious*) or **-tious** (as in *cautious*).

Complete the following definitions with **-ous** words.

1. Risky: ____________________
2. Well known: ____________________
3. Envious: ____________________
4. Consequential: ____________________
5. Full of holes: ____________________
6. Savage: ____________________
7. Resembles a bulb: ____________________
8. Plentiful: ____________________
9. Funny: ____________________
10. Happy: ____________________
11. Apparent: ____________________
12. Not ending: ____________________

barbarous
bulbous
continuous
copious
dangerous
famous
humorous
jealous
joyous
momentous
obvious
porous

Day 112

> **Clue:** When a word ends in a syllable that sounds like...
> - **"-iss,"** it is usually spelled -________ (as in *jealous*).
> - **"-shiss,"** it is usually spelled -________ (as in *precious*) or -________ (as in *cautious*).

Complete the following Scriptures with -**ous** words. One word is used twice.

anxious	jealous	unrighteous
courageous	miraculous	various
generous	prosperous	
glorious	righteous	

1. Joshua 1:8 "For then you will make your way ________________..."
2. 1Timothy 6:18 "They are to ....be____________________________..."
3. Psalm 45:13 "All ___________________ is the princess in her chamber..."
4. Joshua 1:6 "Be strong and ________________________"
5. Exodus 34:14 "...The LORD, whose name is ________________, is a ____________________ God."
6. Mark 6:14 "That is why these _______________________powers are at work in him."
7. James 1:2 "Count it all joy...when you meet trials of ____________________ kinds..."
8. 1 Peter 3:18 "For Christ also suffered once for sins, the _____________________ for the ________________________."
9. Philippians 4:6 "Do not be ____________________ about anything..."

Day 113

Clue: When a word ends in a syllable that sounds like...

- **"-iss,"** it is usually spelled -________ (as in *jealous*).
- **"-shiss,"** it is usually spelled -________ (as in *precious*) or -________ (as in *cautious*).

Complete the clues, then the puzzle, with **-ous** words.

Across

3. Energetic: ________________
4. Awesome: ________________
6. Wondrous: ________________
7. Happy: ________________
8. Noisy: ________________
10. Repugnant: ________________
11. Threatening: ____________________

Down

1. Carefulness in study: ________________
2. Mistaken: ________________
3. Winner: ________________
5. Solemn: ________________
9. Inquisitive: ________________

								1		
						2				
		3								
	4									5
6										
	7									
				8			9			
					10					
		11								

curious	odious	studious
erroneous	ominous	stupendous
joyous	raucous	victorious
marvelous	serious	vigorous

Day 114

> **Clue:** When a word ends in a syllable that sounds like...
> - **"-iss,"** it is usually spelled -________ (as in *jealous*).
> - **"-shiss,"** it is usually spelled -________ (as in *precious*) or -________ (as in *cautious*).

Complete the definitions with **-ous** words.

cantankerous
envious
generous
hazardous
infamous
nauseous
obnoxious
poisonous
ponderous
tedious
tremendous
unscrupulous

1. Offensive: ____________________
2. Upset stomach: ____________________
3. Dangerous: ____________________
4. Without morals: ____________________
5. Boring: ____________________
6. Clumsily heavy: ____________________
7. Venomous: ____________________
8. Giving: ____________________
9. Negatively well-known: ____________________
10. Wonderful: ____________________
11. Jealous: ____________________
12. Grouchy: ____________________

Clue: When a word ends in a syllable that sounds like...

- **"-iss,"** it is usually spelled -________ (as in *jealous*).
- **"-shiss,"** it is usually spelled -________ (as in *precious*) or -________ (as in *cautious*).

Complete the definitions with **-cious** words.

1. Roomy: ____________________
2. Savagely attacking, like angry bees: ____________________
3. Distrustful: ____________________
4. Highly injurious or deadly: ____________________
5. Tasty: ____________________
6. Ravenous: ____________________
7. Sprightly, lively: ____________________
8. Valuable: ____________________
9. Fierce, like a lion: ____________________
10. Forgiving: ____________________
11. Vindictive: ____________________
12. Awake; aware: ____________________
13. Persistently clingy: ____________________

conscious delicious ferocious gracious malicious pernicious precious spacious suspicious tenacious vicious vivacious voracious

Day 116

> **Clue:** When a word ends in a syllable that sounds like…
> - **"-iss,"** it is usually spelled -________ (as in *jealous*).
> - **"-shiss,"** it is usually spelled -________ (as in *precious*) or -________ (as in *cautious*).

Complete the definitions with **-tious** words.

1. Rowdy: ____________________
2. Untimely wittiness: ____________________
3. Careful: ____________________
4. Contagious: ____________________
5. Quarrelsome: ____________________
6. Imaginary: ____________________
7. Irritable: ____________________
8. Showy, gaudy: ____________________
9. Healthy: ____________________
10. Lacking moral restraint: ____________________
11. Annoying: ____________________

cautious
contentious
facetious
fictitious
fractious
infectious
licentious
nutritious
ostentatious
rambunctious
vexatious

Clue: When a word ends in a syllable that sounds like...
- **"-iss,"** it is usually spelled -________ (as in *jealous*).
- **"-shiss,"** it is usually spelled -________ (as in *precious*) or -________ (as in *cautious*).

Complete the Scriptures with **-tious** and **-cious** words. One word is used twice.

contentious deliciously gracious malicious precious

1. Psalm 36:7 "How ____________________ is your steadfast love, O God!"
2. Exodus 34:19 "I will be ____________________ to whom I will be ____________________."
3. 3 John 10 "He...prated against us with ________________ words."
4. Proverb 27:15 "A continual dripping on a very rainy day and a ______________________ woman are alike."
5. Revelation 18:7 "How much she hath glorified herself, and lived ______________________."

Day 118

Clue: When a word ends in a syllable that sounds like...

- **"-iss,"** it is usually spelled -_________ (as in *jealous*).
- **"-shiss,"** it is usually spelled -_________ (as in *precious*) or -_________ (as in *cautious*).

Complete the clues with **-cious** words and **-tious** words, then find the words in the puzzle.

1. Big and roomy: ____________________
2. Valuable: ____________________
3. Distrustful: ____________________
4. Very tasty: ____________________
5. Awake; aware: ____________________
6. Meanly fierce: ____________________
7. Careful: ____________________
8. Healthy: ____________________
9. Make-believe: ____________________
10. Very hungry: ____________________

cautious
conscious
delicious
fictitious
nutritious
precious
spacious
suspicious
vicious
voracious

q	w	e	s	r	t	y	u	i	v	o	p	a
p	s	n	u	t	r	i	t	i	o	u	s	d
r	f	g	o	h	j	k	l	z	r	s	x	s
e	c	c	i	v	b	n	m	q	a	u	u	w
c	a	w	c	a	u	r	e	r	c	o	t	y
i	u	u	i	i	o	p	a	s	i	i	d	f
o	t	f	p	g	h	j	k	c	o	c	k	l
u	i	z	s	p	a	c	i	o	u	s	x	c
s	o	v	u	b	n	l	m	q	s	n	w	e
r	u	t	s	y	e	u	i	o	p	o	a	s
d	s	f	g	d	h	j	k	l	z	c	x	c
v	b	f	i	c	t	i	t	i	o	u	s	n
m	q	w	e	r	t	s	u	o	i	c	i	v

Clue: When a word ends in a syllable that sounds like...

- **"-iss,"** it is usually spelled -_________ (as in *jealous*).
- **"-shiss,"** it is usually spelled -_________ (as in *precious*) or -_________ (as in *cautious*).

Complete the definitions with **-ous** words.

1. Infamous: ___________________________
2. Silly: ______________________
3. In tune: __________________________
4. Plentiful; many: __________________________
5. Preceding: __________________________
6. Anxious: _________________________
7. Unsubmissive: ______________________
8. Catastrophic: _________________________
9. Mutant; monster-like: _________________________
10. Meticulous; high standards: ______________________
11. Moral excellence: ________________________
12. Free from sin: ______________________
13. Beautiful: ________________________
14. Hard; tough: ________________________

callous
disastrous
fastidious
gorgeous
harmonious
monstrous
nervous
notorious
numerous
previous
rebellious
ridiculous
righteous
virtuous

Day 120 Review

Clue: The **long-i-** sound can be spelled a number of different ways, including the following:

- With an -______________ (as in *kite*)
- With a -_________ (as in *try*) if the word ________ in the long -i- sound
- With an -_________ if the word ends with a **long -i** sound **plus -t** (as in *light*). The -_________ is silent.

Clue: The **long -u-** sound can be spelled a number of ways, including:

- _____ (as in *zoo*)
- ___________ (as in *tune*)
- _____ (as in *new*)
- _____ (as in *clue*)

Circle the misspelled words in the sentences below, then write the words correctly on the lines following.

bloom	coon	groom	might	school
blue	disputed	include	moon	tightly
bright	dude	June	mule	
brute	frightened	light	night	
cool	glue	loop	ruler	

1. One nite in Joon the cune dog bayed at the mewn. ______________

_____________________ _____________________ _____________________

2. The broot fritened the dood on the mewl. ______________

_____________________ _____________________ _____________________

3. The grume dispewted with the caterer about placing the wedding cake in the brite lite. ______________

_____________________ _____________________ _____________________

4. The bloo forget-me-nots mite blume in that cule, shady spot.

_____________________ _____________________ _____________________

____

5. Did you remember to inclood a rooler in your schule supplies?

_____________________ _____________________ _____________________

6. The gloo held the lewp titely in place. ______________

_____________________ _____________________

Clue: When a word ends in a syllable that sound like "*-ints*," it is usually spelled one of two ways:

- **-ence** (as in *science*)
- **-ance** (as in *entrance*)

Complete the following definitions with **-ence** words.

1. Ability to sway another's thinking: ____________________
2. Knowledge + skill: ____________________
3. Freedom: ____________________
4. Good at speaking: ____________________
5. Understanding: ____________________
6. Not easily upset: ____________________
7. Nearness: ____________________
8. Submissiveness: ____________________
9. Physical harm: ____________________
10. Unacquainted with evil: ____________________
11. Personal choice: ____________________
12. Around a circle: ____________________
13. Certainty in self: ____________________
14. Carelessness: ____________________
15. Mail: ____________________

circumference confidence correspondence eloquence experience independence influence innocence intelligence negligence obedience patience preference presence violence

Day 122

Clue: When a word ends in a syllable that sound like "*-ints*," it is usually spelled one of two ways:

- ____________ (as in *science*)
- ____________ (as in *entrance*)

Complete the following definitions with **-ance** words.

1. Opposition: ________________
2. Facial expression: ________________
3. Condition: ________________
4. Get back at: ________________
5. Lack of knowledge: ________________
6. Persistence: ________________
7. Received in a will: ________________
8. Opening: ________________
9. Food, water: ________________
10. Excessiveness: ________________
11. Complaint: ________________
12. Significance: ________________
13. Clashing: ________________
14. Influence, authority: ________________
15. Sorrow over sin: ________________

circumstance
countenance
dissonance
dominance
entrance
extravagance
grievance
ignorance
inheritance
importance
perseverance
repentance
resistance
sustenance
vengeance

Clue: When a word ends in a syllable that sound like "*-ints*," it is usually spelled one of two ways:

- ____________ (as in *science*)
- ____________ (as in *entrance*)

Complete the following Scriptures with **-ance** and **-ence** words.

confidence	patience
conscience	presence
countenance	temperance
ignorance	violence

1. 1 Corinthians 10:27 "Eat whatever is set before you without raising any question on the ground of ________________."
2. Galatians 5:22-23 "But the fruit of the Spirit is love, joy, peace, ______________, gentleness, goodness, faith, meekness, __________________..."
3. Psalm 51:11 "Cast me not away from your ________________."
4. Ephesians 4:18 "They are...alienated from the life of God because of the ________________ that is in them..."
5. Hebrews 4:16 "Let us then with __________________ draw near to the throne of grace..."
6. Numbers 6:26 "The LORD lift up His __________________ upon you and give you peace."
7. Isaiah 60:18 "__________________ shall no more be heard in your land."

Day 124

Clue: When a word ends in a syllable that sound like "*-ints*," it is usually spelled one of two ways:

- ______________ (as in *science*)
- ______________ (as in *entrance*)

Complete the clues with **-ance** and **-ence** words, then use those words to complete the crossword puzzle.

Across

3. Stupidity: ________________
7. Plague: ________________
8. Complaint: ________________
9. Superiority: ________________

Down

1. Personal choice: ____________
2. Kind generosity: ____________
4. Carelessness: ______________
5. Submissiveness: ____________
6. Chemistry, biology, etc.: ______________________

												1		
		2		3		4								5
									6					
	7													
						8								
9														

benevolence	negligence	preeminence
grievance	obedience	preference
ignorance	pestilence	science

Clue: When a word ends in a syllable that sound like "*-cher*," it is usually spelled with a *-ture*. For exceptions, see the note in the back of the book.

Correctly spell the words in the chart below by replacing the **-cher** with the correct spelling, **-ture**.

punccher	rapcher
legislacher	denchers
furnicher	leccher
miniacher	feacherd
literacher	advencher

Use the words, spelled correctly, from the chart above to fill in the blanks below.

1. My grandmother left her ________________ in a cup to soak.

2. That tiny dog is called a ________________ poodle.

3. Classics by Mark Twain are considered to be among some of America's greatest works of ______________________.

4. The event where followers of Christ will meet him in the air is commonly called the ________________.

5. We attended a ________________ on the Creation versus Evolution debate.

6. The ________________ flavor was Double Fudge Ripple.

7. If you put tape on it first, you can ________________ a balloon with a needle without popping it.

8. The newly married couple had very little ________________ for their new home.

Day 126

Clue: When a word ends in a syllable that sound like "*-cher*," it is usually spelled with a -__________. For exceptions, see the note in the back of the book.

Complete the puzzle using words ending with **-ture.**

Across
1. Books; classics
3. Your name or John Hancock
4. Past, present, and __________
5. A living thing; monster
6. Table, chairs, beds
8. An action-packed event
10. Inflict excruciating pain
11. Speech

Down
1. The Senate and the House
2. When believers are gone, in a twinkling, with Jesus
4. The showcased flavor or film
6. A broken bone
7. Contractual slavery
9. To lovingly raise

(Answers in alphabetical order: adventure, creature, feature, fracture, furniture, future, indenture, lecture, legislature, literature, nurture, rapture, signature, torture.)

Clue: When a word ends in a syllable that sound like "*-cher*," it is usually spelled with a -__________. For exceptions, see the note in the back of the book.

Correctly spell the words in the chart so that they end with -***ture***.

torcherd	nurcher	pascher
picchers	Scripcher	creacher
nacher	furnicher	fucher

Complete the verses with correctly-spelled words from the chart.

1. "...the Tent of Meeting, the Ark of the Testimony with the atonement cover on it, and all the other ________________..." Exodus 31:7

2. "It is He who made us, and we are His; we are His people, the sheep of His ______________________." Psalm 100:3

3. "A word aptly spoken is like apples of gold in _______________ of silver." Proverbs 25:11

4. "For I know the thoughts that I think toward you...thoughts of peace and not of evil, to give you a _______________ and a hope." Jeremiah 29:11

5. "Go into all the world and preach the gospel to every ___________________." Mark 16:15

6. "Do not provoke your children to wrath, but bring them up in the __________________ and admonition of the Lord." Ephesians 6:4

7. "All ________________________ is given by inspiration of God..." 2 Timothy 3:16

8. "Others were ____________________, not accepting deliverance." Hebrews 11:35

9. "...You may be partakers of the divine ____________." 2 Pet. 1:4

Day 128

Clue: When a word ends in a syllable that sound like "*-cher*," it is usually spelled with a -__________. For exceptions, see the note in the back of the book.

Correctly spell each of the words in the chart so that they end with the syllable *-ture*.

tinccher	macher
miniacher	literacher
fixcher	advenchers
sucher	deparcher
indencher	feacherd

Complete these sentences with correctly-spelled words from the chart:

1. We had many ____________________ when we went to Ocean City for vacation.

2. Our vacation ____________________ several unusual happenings and even mishaps.

3. It rained so much, I guess you could say that bad weather was a ________________ for that vacation.

4. While fishing, the boys accidentally hooked a fully-______________ sea gull by the wing.

5. Though it would have been nice to _______________ the wound and put _______________ of iodine on it, the large, frantic bird would allow no such thing!

6. Between rain storms, the ground around our campsite was crawling with _________________ crabs, no bigger around than a quarter.

7. There were many other adventures, most of them enjoyable, and the time of our _________________ brought sadness.

Clue: When a word ends in a syllable that sound like "*-cher*," it is usually spelled with a -___________. For exceptions, see the note in the back of the book.

There are nine misspelled ***-ture*** words in the story below. Circle them, then write them correctly on the lines at the bottom.

William Penn was a great man of God. He lived in a time when Christians were commonly torcherd for their faith. He himself became a Christian as a youth. Once he made the commitment to follow God, his life was never the same. He just moved from one advencher to another.

Penn, a lawyer, spent much of his life defending Christians in court. In those days macher Christians would rather die for their faith than deny Christ. The English legislacher had already passed laws allowing the people the right to a fair trial, but few courts of that day practiced the law, especially when it came to trying Christians. Penn was determined to fight for this right - and he was thrown into prison for his pains.

Actually, Penn wasn't a stranger to prison. He had been capcherd and thrown in prison a number of times for preaching the gospel. He gave up much more, though, than just his freedom for the sake of the gospel. His father, the Admiral, hounded him much of his life to give up his religion. The Admiral leccherd him, threatened him, and even disinherited him. Penn actually came from a very wealthy family that held high position in the King's court, but Penn gave it all up for Jesus.

Eventually the Lord led William Penn to establish a colony where the government was based on Scripcher. The King of England himself placed his signacher on the charter that granted Penn that vast wilderness territory that we know today as Pennsylvania. In this new colony, Christians would finally be able to live in peace, to practice their faith freely, and to offer their children a fucher full of hope.

_______________ _______________ _______________

_______________ _______________ _______________

_______________ _______________ _______________

Day 130 Review

> **Clue:** The **long-i-** sound can be spelled a number of different ways, including the following:
> - With an -_______________ (as in *kite*)
> - With a -__________ (as in *try*) if the word ________ in the long -i- sound
> - With an -__________ if the word ends with a **long -i** sound **plus -t** (as in *light*). The -__________ is silent.

> **Clue:** The following words are tricky and should be memorized.
> - The word ***why*** has a silent -______-
> - ***Does*** is verb __________ with an -_____ on the end
> - ***Only*** has a ___________ sound
> - ***Who*** has a silent _____. It rhymes with ______ (which also has a silent -__-)

> **Clue:** The **long -e** sound in the ***middle*** of a word is usually spelled one of two ways:
> - With and ________ as in *feet,*
> - With an _________ as in *meat.*

Circle the incorrect words in the sentences below, then write them correctly on the lines following.

1. Wy duz the baby screem all the tym? ____________
____________ ____________ ____________

2. He ownly eets beaf and cherry py. ____________
____________ ____________ ____________

3. Hoo is the guy that fell off his byke and skinned his kneas?
____________ ____________ ____________

4. How duz the pryce on those tyres compare with this deel?
____________ ____________ ____________
____

5. Wy duz the quean bea seldom leeve the hyve? ____________
____________ ____________ ____________
____________ ____________

Clue: Contractions are two words put together to form one word. An apostrophe is used to mark the missing letters.

- In most contractions, the spelling of the first word doesn't change.
- Instead, two words are squeezed together and letters are left out.
- An apostrophe is placed where the letters used to be.
- The trick is to remember how to spell the two words, don't change the spelling, and put an apostrophe where the missing letters used to be.

List the letter(s) that were replaced by an apostrophe in the following contractions:

Contraction	Missing Letters	Contraction	Missing Letters
doesn't		you'd	
isn't		wouldn't	
I'll		could've	
that's		you're	
they're		would've	
you'll		they'll	
she'd		we're	

Add the appropriate contractions to the sentences below.

1. I _______________(do not) know where _______________(you are) supposed to put those.
2. I suppose _______________(you will) figure out a spot for them.
3. We _________________ (could have) sold them at a yard sale.
4. You _________________(would not) have wanted to do that, though.
5. _______________ (they will) probably have sentimental value attached to them.
6. __________(that is) why __________(you would) rather keep them.
7. I know _____________(she would) be interested in buying them from you.

Day 132

Clue: Contractions are ________ words put together to form _________word. An apostrophe is used to mark the _______________ letters.

- In most contractions, the spelling of the first word _____________ change.
- Instead, two words are __________ together and letters are _________ ________.
- An apostrophe is placed where the letters __________ _____ _____.
- The trick is to remember how to __________ the two words, don't _________ the spelling, and put an apostrophe where the missing letters _________ ____ ____.

What two words make up each of the contractions below?

Contraction	Two Words	Contraction	Two Words
can't		she's	
you're		shouldn't	
hasn't		hadn't	
weren't		could've	
it's		they're	
we're		you'll	
he'll		aren't	

Use the correct contraction in the sentences below.

1. "God _____________(did not) send His Son into the world to condemn the world, but to save the world through Him." Jn. 3:17

2. "___________(do not) be deceived. God __________(is not) mocked. Whatever a man sows, that ___________(he will) also reap." Galatians 6:7

3. "If we confess our sins, __________(He is) faithful and just to forgive us...and to cleanse us from...unrighteousness." 1 Jn. 1:9

4. "Put away lying. Speak every man truth with his neighbor, for ______________(we are) members one of another." Eph. 4:25

5. "__________(I am) confident of this very thing, that He which has begun a good work in you will perform it." (Phil. 1:6)

6. "__________(I have) hidden your Word in my heart." Ps. 119:11

Clue: Contractions are ________ words put together to form _________word. An apostrophe is used to mark the _______________ letters.

- In most contractions, the spelling of the first word ______________ change.
- Instead, two words are __________ together and letters are _________ _______.
- An apostrophe is placed where the letters ___________ _____ _____.
- The trick is to remember how to __________ the two words, don't _________ the spelling, and put an apostrophe where the missing letters _________ ____ ____.

Turn the words below into contractions. List the letters that were replaced by an apostrophe.

Words	Contraction	Missing Letters	Words	Contraction	Missing Letters
does not			can not		
we have			were not		
they have			we are		
I would			they would		
he is			I am		
we will			who will		
has not			they are		
who is			you will		

Use the correct contractions in Scriptures below.

1. "___________ (There is) now no condemnation for those who are in Christ Jesus." Romans 8:1
2. "For _________________ (nothing is) impossible with God." Lk. 1:37
3. "_________ (I will) praise You, Lord, with all my heart." Ps. 9:1
4. "________ (It is) written, 'Man shall not live by bread alone, but by every word...from the mouth of god.'" Matthew 4:4
5. "Delight yourself in the Lord, and __________ (He will) give thee the desires of your heart." Psalm 37:4
6. "Without faith _______(it is) impossible to please God." Heb. 11:6
7. "________(We have) all sinned and fallen short of God's glory." Romans 3:23

Day 134

Clue: Contractions are ________ words put together to form ________ word. An apostrophe is used to mark the ______________ letters.

- In most contractions, the spelling of the first word ____________ change.
- Instead, two words are __________ together and letters are _________ ________.
- An apostrophe is placed where the letters _________ ______ ______.
- The trick is to remember how to __________ the two words, don't _________ the spelling, and put an apostrophe where the missing letters ________ ____ ____.

Turn the words below into contractions. List the letters that were replaced by an apostrophe.

Words	Contraction	Missing Letters	Words	Contraction	Missing Letters
are not			have not		
should not			has not		
she is			it is		
who will			they will		
we will			we are		
they are			I would		
we would			you are		

Use the correct contractions in the sentences below.

1. ____________________ (Would not) you enjoy playing in our band?
2. ____________________(You are) sure?
3. ____________________(We have) got two guitars and a bass.
4. We ____________(are not) professionals, but we enjoy praising God.
5. We also have a drum set, but I think ______________(they are) too loud to enjoy.
6. _____________(Is not) it amazing how quickly you can learn something when you enjoy it?
7. Why ________________(do not) you join us for worship the next time ______________(it is) convenient.

Clue: The ***-er*** sound in a word is usually spelled one of three ways:

- ***-ur*** (as in *purse*)
- ***-ir*** (as in *shirt*)
- ***-er*** (as in *term*). This spelling is often found at the *end* of a word.

Complete the following definitions with ***-ur*** words.

1. Set time to be home: ____________________
2. Injured: ________________
3. Sudden growth or action: _________________
4. Clinging seed: ____________________
5. Unclear: ________________
6. Corkscrews: ____________________
7. Unfold: ________________
8. Medical person: __________________
9. Over-cook; char: ___________________
10. Territory: ________________
11. Foggy, hazy: _______________
12. To make butter: ______________
13. To ride waves: ______________
14. Thanksgiving bird: ______________
15. Belch: _______________

blurry
burn
burp
burr
churn
curfew
curls
hurt
murky
nurse
spurt
surf
turf
turkey
unfurl

Day 136

> **Clue:** The *-er* sound in a word is usually spelled one of three ways:
> - ________ (as in *purse*)
> - ________ (as in *shirt*)
> - ________ (as in *term*). This spelling is often found at the *end* of a word.

Complete the following definitions with *-ir* words.

1. Article of clothing: ____________________
2. Soil: ____________________
3. Beam: ____________________
4. The number 30: ____________________
5. Eagle, robin, sparrow, etc.: ____________________
6. Mix or whip: ____________________
7. 3rd: ____________________
8. Female: ____________________
9. A male's formal address: ____________________
10. Twist: ____________________
11. Type of tree: ____________________
12. Avoid: ____________________
13. Unyielding: ____________________
14. Wiggle: ____________________
15. Bird sound: ____________________

birch
bird
chirp
dirt
firm
girder
girl
shirk
shirt
sir
squirm
stir
swirl
third
thirty

Clue: The *-er* sound in a word is usually spelled one of three ways:

- ________ (as in *purse*)
- ________ (as in *shirt*)
- ________ (as in *term*). This spelling is often found at the *end* of a word.

Complete the following definitions with ***-er*** words.

1. Not him: ________________
2. Type of race: ________________
3. Action word: ________________
4. Extent of time: ________________
5. Scent to wear: ________________
6. Unflawed: ________________
7. Floating ice mountain: ________________
8. Virus, bacteria: ________________
9. What a bird sits on: ________________
10. Relating to heat: ________________
11. European country: ________________
12. Shade-loving plant: ________________
13. Stanza: ________________
14. Fiber for feeling:________________
15. Not temporary: ________________

derby fern germ Germany her iceberg nerve perch perfect perfume permanent term thermal verb verse

Day 138

Clue: The *-er* sound in a word is usually spelled one of three ways:

- _______ (as in *purse*)
- _______ (as in *shirt*)
- _______ (as in *term*). This spelling is often found at the *end* of a word.

Complete the clues with ***-ur***, ***-ir***, and ***-er*** words, then find them in the puzzle.

1. Female garment: ________________
2. Need liquids: ________________
3. To kill: ________________
4. Hide in wait: ________________
5. Fuzzy: ________________
6. Unchanging: ________________
7. Worry: ________________
8. Human: ________________
9. To draw attention of opposite sex: ________________
10. Spray: ________________
11. Hex: ________________
12. Zealous: ________________

concern
curse
fervent
flirt
furry
lurk
murder
permanent
person
skirt
squirt
thirsty

q	w	e	r	t	y	u	i	o	p	f	c
p	a	s	k	i	r	t	s	d	f	e	o
f	e	g	h	m	j	h	k	l	l	r	n
z	t	r	x	c	u	i	i	v	b	v	c
n	m	n	s	q	w	r	e	r	t	e	e
y	u	i	e	o	t	s	d	o	p	n	r
a	s	d	f	n	n	t	g	e	h	t	n
e	s	r	u	c	a	y	j	k	r	u	l
k	l	z	x	c	v	m	m	b	n	m	q
s	q	u	i	r	t	w	r	g	e	r	t
y	u	i	o	p	a	s	d	e	i	f	g
h	j	k	l	f	u	r	r	y	p	o	z

Clue: The *-er* sound in a word is usually spelled one of three ways:

- _______ (as in *purse*)
- _______ (as in *shirt*)
- _______ (as in *term*). This spelling is often found at the *end* of a word.

Complete the following Scriptures with *-ur*, *-ir*, and *-er* words.

adversary	first
church	murder
curse	perfume
fervent	purchased
firm	purpose

1. 1 Peter 5:8-9 "Your _________________ the devil prowls around like a roaring lion...Resist him, ___________ in your faith..."
2. 1 John 4:19 "We love because He _____________ loved us."
3. Exodus 20:13 "You shall not _________________."
4. Luke 6:28 "Bless those who _______________ you."
5. Acts 20:28 "...The Holy Ghost has made you overseers, to feed the _____________ of God, which He has __________________ with His own blood."
6. Proverb 27:9 "Oil and ________________ make the heart glad..."
7. Romans 12:11 "...Be _____________ in spirit."
8. Isaiah 46:10 "I will accomplish all my __________________."

Day 140 Review

> **Clue:** When a word ends in a syllable that sounds like...
> - **"-iss,"** it is usually spelled -_________ (as in *jealous*).
> - **"-shiss,"** it is usually spelled -_________ (as in *precious*) or -_________ (as in *cautious*).

> **Clue:** When a word ends in a syllable that sound like "***-ints***," it is usually spelled one of two ways:
> - _______________ (as in *science*)
> - _______________ (as in *entrance*)

> **Clue:** When a word ends in a syllable that sound like "***-cher***," it is usually spelled with a -____________. For exceptions, see the note in the back of the book.

Circle the misspelled words, then write them correctly on the lines following.

anxious	glorious	presence
assurance	instance	radiance
audience	lecture	silence
dangerous	nature	violence
difference		

1. I remember one instints where the audients greeted the end of the long leccher with complete silints. ______________________

   ______________________ ______________________ ______________________

2. The differints between Christians and non-Christians is that we have the assurints of the presints of God because of the work of His death on the cross, so we need never be anxshis.

   ______________________ ______________________ ______________________

   ____

3. Nacher is often both dangeriss and gloriuss, exhibiting both violints and radiints. ______________________ ______________________

   ______________________ ______________________ ______________________

Clue: The words ***could***, ***should***, and ***would*** all end in the same four letters: ***-ould***.

Complete the Scriptures below with ***should***, ***could***, and ***would***.

1. Psalm 24:12 "Him will he instruct in the way that he _____________ (shood) choose."
2. Psalm 78:7 "...They _____________(shood) set their hope in God..."
3. Psalm 84:10 "...I _____________(wud) rather be a doorkeeper in the house of my God..."
4. Psalm 124:2-3 "If it had not been the LORD who was on our side...then they _____________(wud) have swallowed us up alive..."
5. Psalm 37:36 "Though I sought [the wicked man], he _____________ (cood) not be found."
6. Romans 8:3 "For God has done what the law..._______________ (cood) not do."
7. Matthew 26:40 "_______________ (cood) you not watch with me one hour?"

Day 142

Clue: The words *could*, *should*, and *would* all end in the same four letters:__________.

Complete the Scriptures below with ***should***, ***could***, and ***would***.

1. Job 31:23 "I ______________(cood) not have faced His majesty."
2. Psalm 49:5 "Why ______________(shood) I fear in times of trouble?"
3. Matthew 17:16 "They ______________(cood) not heal him."
4. Psalm 81:13 "Oh, that my people ______________(wud) listen to me."
5. Psalm 78:6-7 "...Tell them to their children, so that they ______________(shood) set their hope in God..."
6. Psalm 143:8 "Make me know the way I ______________(shood) go..."
7. Song of Solomon 8:1 "If I found you outside, I ______________(wud) kiss you, and none ______________(wud) despise me."

Clue: The words ***could***, ***should***, and ***would*** all end in the same four letters:____________.

Complete the Scriptures below with ***should***, ***could***, and ***would***.

1. Job 31:37 "I __________________(wud) give Him an account of all my steps..."
2. Daniel 5:8 "They _________________(cood) not read the writing..."
3. Proverb 2:16 "Train up a child in the way he _______________ (shud) go..."
4. Acts 13:38-39 "And by Him everyone who believes is freed from everything from which you ________________(cood) not be freed by the law..."
5. Isaiah 53:2 "He had no form or majesty that we ______________ (shood) look at Him, and no beauty that we _________________ (shood) desire Him."
6. Hebrews 12:20 "For they ________________(cood) not endure the order that was given."
7. Daniel 5:19 "Whom He _________________(wud), He killed, and whom He ________________(wud), He kept alive; whom He _______________ (wud), He raised up, and whom He _______________ (wud) He humbled."

Day 144

> **Clue:** When a *short-vowel* word or syllable *ends* with a ***-j*** sound, the ***-j*** sound is usually spelled with a ***-dge*** (as in *edge*).
> When a *short-vowel* word or syllable *ends* with a ***-ch*** sound, the ***-ch*** sound is usually spelled with a ***-tch*** (as in *catch*).
> For exceptions to this rule, see the notes in the back of this book.

Spell the ***-dge*** words in the chart correctly, then use them (spelled correctly) to complete the sentences below.

ej	plej	juj
drej	gruj	loj
hej	fuj	nuj

1. In a marriage ceremony, you ________________ yourself to another until death parts you.

2. A __________________ presides over a trial, which is conducted before a jury of peers.

3. A rich, chocolate treat that tastes good when heated and poured over ice cream is called __________________.

4. In the pinewood derby race, each boy had to give his car a small __________________ to get it going as the signal sounded.

5. Another name for a cabin or dwelling in the woods is a ____________________.

6. Bushes and plants that form a barrier between two areas are known as a ____________________.

7. When a river bottom gets clogged with debris, workers can __________________ it to clear it.

8. If I stand too close to the ______________ of a steep cliff, I get very dizzy.

9. When someone offends you, and you stay angry at that person, that is called "holding a __________________."

Clue: When a *short-vowel* word or syllable *ends* with a *-j* sound, the ____ sound is usually spelled with a _________ (as in *edge*).
When a *short-vowel* word or syllable *ends* with a *-ch* sound, the _____ sound is usually spelled with a _________ (as in *catch*).
For exceptions to this rule, see the notes in the back of this book.

Fill in the blanks in the clues, then find the ***-dge*** words in the word-search puzzle below.

a	s	d	f	g	h	j	k	l	q	e	r	e	r	t	y	e	u	i
b	o	p	z	x	c	v	b	n	q	a	e	r	g	t	g	y	u	o
u	i	a	s	d	f	g	e	h	j	k	l	z	x	d	c	v	b	n
d	q	e	r	t	t	e	g	d	i	m	y	u	i	i	e	o	p	a
g	s	d	f	g	h	j	d	k	l	z	x	r	c	g	v	b	n	m
e	e	r	t	y	u	i	a	o	p	a	b	s	a	d	f	g	h	j
t	k	l	z	x	c	v	b	b	n	q	e	d	r	t	y	u	i	o
t	k	s	d	f	g	h	j	k	l	z	g	z	s	l	e	d	g	e
x	h	o	d	g	e	p	o	d	g	e	c	v	m	b	n	q	e	r
t	y	u	r	i	o	p	a	r	t	s	d	f	u	g	h	j	k	l
z	x	c	e	v	b	n	q	u	e	r	t	y	d	u	i	o	p	a
s	d	f	d	g	h	j	k	d	l	z	x	c	g	v	b	n	q	e
r	t	y	g	u	i	o	p	g	r	u	d	g	e	a	s	d	f	g
h	j	k	e	l	z	x	c	e	c	v	b	n	q	e	r	t	y	u

Clues:

1. Identifies police: ________________
2. Hard working slave: ________________
3. Financial planning: ________________
4. To clear a river bottom: ____________
5. A type of hammer: ________________
6. A very short person: ______________
7. Gizmo: ________________
8. Staying angry: ____________
9. Mish-mash: ________________
10. Border: ________________
11. Smear: ________________
12. Spans water: ____________

(Use these words: badge, bridge, budget, dredge, drudge, edge, gadget, grudge, hodgepodge, midget, sledge, smudge)

Day 146

Clue: When a *short-vowel* word or syllable *ends* with a *-j* sound, the ____ sound is usually spelled with a ________ (as in *edge*).
When a *short-vowel* word or syllable *ends* with a *-ch* sound, the ____ sound is usually spelled with a ________ (as in *catch*).
For exceptions to this rule, see the notes in the back of this book.

Spell the words in the chart correctly, then use them (spelled correctly), to complete the Bible verses below. Some words are used several times.

bajr	ej	gruj
hej	juj	lejs
plej	loj	wej

1. "The LORD shall ____________ the peoples; ______________ me, O LORD, according to my righteousness..." Psalm 7:8
2. "And they will fall by the ____________ of the sword, and be led away captive into all nations." Luke 21:24
3. "______________not one against another, brethren, lest you be condemned..." James 5:9
4. "Have you not made a ____________ around him, around his household, and around all that he has on every side?" Job 1:10
5. "Wherever you go, I will go; and wherever you ___________, I will _____________; Your people shall be my people, and your God, my God." Ruth 1:16
6. "You shall not pervert justice due the stranger or the fatherless, nor take a widow's garment as a ______________." Deut. 24:17
7. "Over the golden altar they shall spread a blue cloth, and cover it with a covering of ________________ skins..." Numbers 4:11
8. "And on the borders that were between the ____________ were lions, oxen, and cherubims: and upon the _____________ there was a base above..." 1 Kings 7:29
9. "When I saw among the spoils a beautiful Babylonian garment, 200 shekels of silver, and a ___________ of gold weighing 50 shekels, I coveted them and took them." Joshua 7:21

Clue: When a *short-vowel* word or syllable *ends* with a *-j* sound, the ____ sound is usually spelled with a ________ (as in *edge*).
When a *short-vowel* word or syllable *ends* with a *-ch* sound, the ____ sound is usually spelled with a ________ (as in *catch*).
For exceptions to this rule, see the notes in the back of this book.

Using the clues given, write the correct *-tch* word in the blank.

batch	catch	crutch	ditch
Dutch	fetch	match	patch
pitch	scratch	watch	witch

1. A word to describe a toss or throw of a ball: ______________
2. A stick with a coated end used to start a fire: ______________
3. To receive a ball that has been tossed to you: ______________
4. An evil person who derives power from Satan, and uses that power to curse people or direct their destinies: ______________
5. A prop that you use when you break a leg: ______________
6. A small clock that you wear on your wrist: ______________
7. One group of cookies is called a ______________ of cookies.
8. Jack and Jill went up the hill to ______________ a pail of water.
9. A cat's unsheathed claws may ______________ you.
10. People from Holland or the Netherlands are ______________.
11. A long trench used for drainage is a ______________.
12. A hole in your pants can be covered with a ______________.

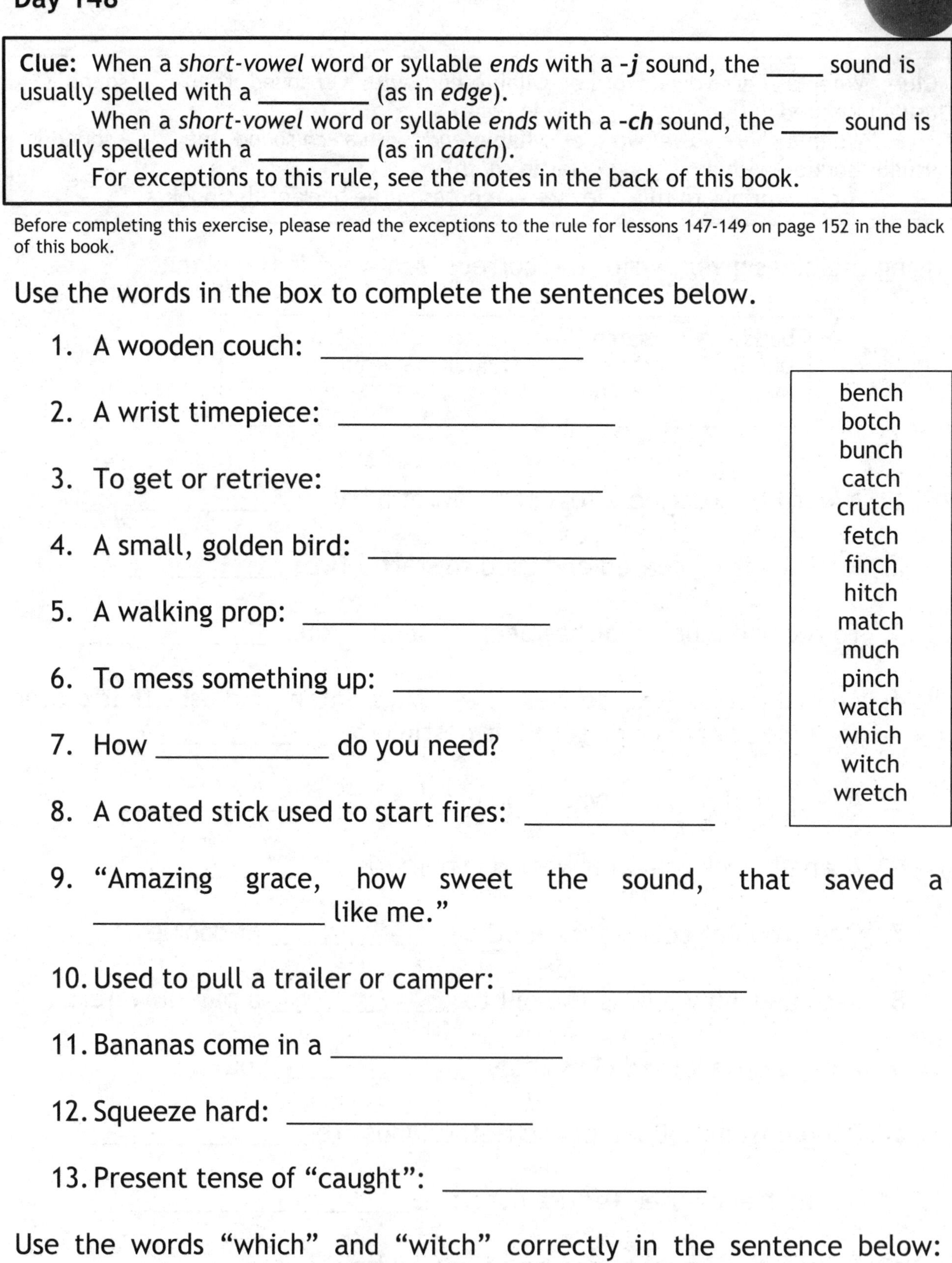

Day 148

Clue: When a *short-vowel* word or syllable *ends* with a *-j* sound, the ____ sound is usually spelled with a ________ (as in *edge*).

When a *short-vowel* word or syllable *ends* with a *-ch* sound, the ____ sound is usually spelled with a ________ (as in *catch*).

For exceptions to this rule, see the notes in the back of this book.

Before completing this exercise, please read the exceptions to the rule for lessons 147-149 on page 152 in the back of this book.

Use the words in the box to complete the sentences below.

bench
botch
bunch
catch
crutch
fetch
finch
hitch
match
much
pinch
watch
which
witch
wretch

1. A wooden couch: ________________
2. A wrist timepiece: ________________
3. To get or retrieve: ________________
4. A small, golden bird: ________________
5. A walking prop: ________________
6. To mess something up: ________________
7. How ____________ do you need?
8. A coated stick used to start fires: ______________
9. "Amazing grace, how sweet the sound, that saved a ________________ like me."
10. Used to pull a trailer or camper: ________________
11. Bananas come in a ________________
12. Squeeze hard: ________________
13. Present tense of "caught": ________________

Use the words "which" and "witch" correctly in the sentence below:

____________ ______________ is ______________?

> **Clue:** When a *short-vowel* word or syllable *ends* with a *-j* sound, the ____ sound is usually spelled with a ________ (as in *edge*).
> When a *short-vowel* word or syllable *ends* with a *-ch* sound, the ____ sound is usually spelled with a ________ (as in *catch*).
> For exceptions to this rule, see the notes in the back of this book.

Find and circle the misspelled words in the sentences below. Write the words correctly on the lines provided. *In order to complete this lesson properly, you must study the exception note for this lesson in the back of the book on page 152.*

1. We lit a tortch for Christmas, and placed it on the front portch of the churtch. The flame grew too large and almost caught the birtch tree on fire! ________________ ________________ ________________ ________________

2. I had a huntch my mother was in a pintch when our cousins stopped by unexpectedly! We were just getting ready to eat luntch, so she invited them in to join us. Mom can make any meal strech! ________________ ________________ ________________ ________________

3. Did you ever wach someone who is learning to drive? It's funny how they'll pop the cluch and lurtch forward. It always makes me flintch when I have to ride with a new driver! ________________ ________________ ________________ ________________

4. Once I heard this "cruntch" sound in the cabinet. I figured it was a mouse, so I grabbed the cat, carefully lifted the lach, and threw her in! Well, she didn't want to muntch on mouse! She just wanted me to scrach her back! She's no help at all! ________________ ________________ ________________ ________________

Day 150 Review

Clue: When a word ends in a syllable that sounds like...

- **"-iss,"** it is usually spelled -________ (as in *jealous*).
- **"-shiss,"** it is usually spelled -________ (as in *precious*) or -________ (as in *cautious*).

Clue: Contractions are ________ words put together to form ________word. An apostrophe is used to mark the ______________ letters.

- In most contractions, the spelling of the first word ____________ change.
- Instead, two words are _________ together and letters are ________ _______.
- An apostrophe is placed where the letters _________ ____ _____.
- The trick is to remember how to _________ the two words, don't ________ the spelling, and put an apostrophe where the missing letters ________ ___ ___.

Clue: The *-er* sound in a word is usually spelled one of three ways:

- _______ (as in *purse*)
- _______ (as in *shirt*)
- _______ (as in *term*). This spelling is often found at the *end* of a word.

Circle the misspelled words in the sentences below, then write the words correctly on the lines following.

1. That terkey dinner cant possibly be both delishiss *and* nutrishiss.

   ________________ ________________ ________________

   ____

2. Isnt that raucis gerl with the cerly hair at least therty years old?

   ________________ ________________ ________________

   ________________ ________________

3. Your perple shert doesnt match that gorgiss skert.

   ________________ ________________ ________________

   ________________ ________________

4. Ill probably get nerviss riding in that dangeriss dirby.

   ________________ ________________ ________________

   ____

5. That ridiculiss nerse didnt wash the girms from her derty hands.

   ________________ ________________ ________________

   ________________ ________________

(Use these words: can't, curly, dangerous, delicious, derby, didn't, dirty, doesn't, germs, girl, gorgeous, I'll, isn't, nervous, nurse, nutritious, purple, raucous, ridiculous, shirt, skirt, thirty, turkey)

Notes concerning Exceptions

Lessons 1-9 (Long -a...)

There are at least two other ways to spell the long -a sound, but they are not used often. They are:

- -ey (as in *obey* and *they*)
- -ei (as in *weigh, their,* and *eight*)

Lessons 11-15 (i before e except after c...)

The trick here is to realize there are several other ways to spell the long -e sound besides -ie. These are reviewed in lessons 71-79. One exception to the *i before e* rule is the word *height* which has the long -I sound, but is spelled with and -ei. Another exception is *leisure.*

Lessons 35-39 (The -oi- sound...)

The -oi- sound in the *middle* of a word has a few exceptions (which are not used often), such as -aw- (as in *lawyer*) and -oy- (as in *foyer*).

Lessons 51-59 (Long -o...)

There are at least four other ways to spell the long -o sound, but they are not used often. They are:

- -ow (as in *know, snow, and own*)
- -oe (as in *toe* and *Joe*)
- -old (as in *sold, gold,* and *told*)
- -ost (as in *host, most,* and *post*)

Lessons 61-65 (The short -o- sound...)

There are several other ways to spell this sound, including...

- -o- (as in *frog* and *dog*)
- -ough- (as in *cough* and *bought*)
- -al- (as in *walk* and *calm*)

Lessons 71-79 (Long -e...)

There are several other ways to spell the long -e sound. The first two are not used often. They are:

- -e+consonant+silent -e (as in *scene, these,* and *here*)
- -ey (as in *key, money,* and *donkey*)
- -ie (as in *field, thief,* and *belief*)

Also, a number of long -e words also *end* in a silent -e. Study these examples: *believe, cheese, sleeve, please, peace, leave.*

Lessons 81-89 (Long -u...)

There are a couple of other ways to spell the long -u- sound, including:

- -ui- (as in *fruit, bruise,* and *juice*)
- -oe- (as in *shoe*)
- -o+consonant+silent -e (as in *move*)

Page 152

Lessons 91-99 (Long -i...)

Long -i- can be spelled with an -igh (as in *sigh, thigh,* and *high*). It can also be spelled with a -ye (as in *bye* and *rye*) or a -uy (as in *buy* and *guy*).

Lessons 111-119 (The -ous, -cious, and -tious sound...)

This sound can also be spelled with an -ice (as in *apprentice, novice, practice,* and *hospice*). The suffix -ness can also have the same sound (as in *happiness, joyfulness, loveliness, holiness,* etc.).

Lessons 121-124 (The -ints sound)

This sound can be spelled with an -ense (as in *pretense* and *defense*). This sound can also be made when a word that ends in -ant or -ent (such as *pennant* and *parent*) are made plural (*pennants* and *parents*).

Lessons 125-129 (Ending syllable spelled -ture)

There are a few *root* words that end in -ch or -tch that add the ***suffix -er***, such as *teacher, preacher,* and *pitcher*. In these cases, the -cher sound at the end is not spelled with -ture. Just remember these words have a root that ***can stand alone*** (*teach, preach, pitch*).

Lessons 131-134 (Contractions)

Most contractions follow the rules. The exception is the common contraction for *will + not*. It is spelled *won't*.

Lessons 135-139 (-er, -ir, -ur...)

The -er sound can be spelled with any of the five vowels, including -or- (as in *terror, minor, doctor,* and *sailor*) and -ar- (as in *calendar, liar, leopard, mustard,* and *buzzard*).

Lessons 144-146 (Ending -j sound spelled as -dge...)

There are several words that end with a -j sound but are spelled with a -ge rather than a -dge. These words have long-vowel sounds rather than short vowel sounds (*cage, rage, sage*).

Lessons 147-149 (Ending -ch sound is spelled with a -tch...)

There are several common words that are exceptions to this rule, such as *which, much,* and *such*. *Teach, preach,* and *reach* have long vowel sounds, so they end only in -ch. Also, if a word ends with another consonant plus the -ch sound, then you don't use the silent -t (like -rch as in *porch, perch,* and *torch* OR -nch as in *lunch, bench,* and *pinch*).

State Abbreviations for use in Lessons 106-109

AL - Alabama
AK - Alaska
AZ - Arizona
AR -Arkansas
CA - California
CO - Colorado
CT - Connecticut
DE - Delaware
FL - Florida
GA - Georgia
HI - Hawaii
ID - Idaho
IL - Illinois
IN - Indiana
IA - Iowa
KS - Kansas
KY - Kentucky
LA - Louisiana
ME - Maine
MD - Maryland
MA - Massachusetts
MI - Michigan
MN - Minnesota
MS - Mississippi
MO - Missouri
MT - Montana
NE - Nebraska
NV - Nevada
NH - New Hampshire
NJ - New Jersey
NM - New Mexico
NY - New York
NC - North Carolina
ND - North Dakota
OH - Ohio
OK - Oklahoma
OR - Oregon
PA - Pennsylvania
RI - Rhode Island
SC - South Carolina
SD - South Dakota
TN - Tennessee
TX - Texas
UT - Utah
VT - Vermont
VA - Virginia
WA - Washington
WV - West Virginia
WI - Wisconsin
WY - Wyoming

Page 154

Answer Key

Day 1: 1. Cane; 2. Space; 3. Made; 4. Stare; 5. Maze; 6. Sale; 7. Bare; 8. Bake; 9. Fate, Dave, Nate; 10. Trade, sane.

Day 2: clue: -ai, -a, -e, -ay; 1. hates; 2. flames; 3. blame; 4. blade, came; 5. share, sale; 6. faces, pale; 7. came, became, lanes, lame.

Day 3: 1. chases, shame; 2. slave; 3. trade; 4. place, gate; 5. name, take, face, made; 6. place, shake; 7. whale.

Day 4: 1. jade; 2. made; 3. cape; 4. fade; 5. fame; 6. game; 7. state; 8. grade; 9. slate; 10. wade; 11. shade; 12. cake; 13. pace; 14. ape; 15. drape; 16. save.

Day 5: 1. waited; 2. trained; 3. main; 4. rain; 5. main, trail; 6. waiting, pain; 7. fails; 8. gain; 9. remain; 10. paid.

Day 6: 1. faith, grain; 2. praise, praise; 3. laid; 4. saint; 5. afraid, sail; 6. Spain; 7. braided, hair; 8. tail, tail, pair, tails.

Day 7: 1. bait; 2. maid; 3. chair; 4. tail; 5. snail; 6. mail; 7. jail; 8. hail; 9. raid; 10. brain; 11. drain; 12. vain; 13. pair; 14. fair; 15. stairs.

Day 8: 1. lay; 2. play; 3. pray; 4. day; 5. delay; 6. lay, hay, day; 7. day, day, display; 8. gray.

Day 9: 1. bay; 2. jay; 3. flay; 4. stray; 5. dismay; 6. bray; 7. may; 8. pay; 9. gay; 10. decay; 11. tray; 12. say; 13. slay; 14. stay; 15. way; 16. fray; 17. ray; 18. spray; 19. away.

Day 10: 1. lay, pray, wake, pray, take; 2. scare, mare, glare, flare, spare; 3. brain, drain; 4. day, today, makes, rain; 5. same, saved; 6. remains, jay, decay; 7. wait, faith; 8. made, snakes, snails, tails; 9. take, paces, grave, gate, delay, shade.

Day 11: friend (A), ceiling (b), weigh (c), neighbor (c), believe (a), retrieve (a), deceitful (b), field (a), Daniel (a), thief (a), eight (c), piece (a), yield (a), tie (a); 1. retriever (a), Daniel (a); 2. eight (c), weighs (c); 3. neighbors (c), friend (a); 4. thief (a), piece (a); 5. believe (a), ceiling (b), retrieve (a), weigh (c); 6. tie (a), field (a); 7. deceitful (b).

Day 12: Clue: -I, -e, -c, -a, -ei, -ei, -ie; lie(a); their (c); heir (c); yield (a), deceived (b), die (a), conceive (b), patient (a), field (a), neighbor (c), quiet (a), chief (a), friend (a), receive (b), believe (a); 1. conceive; 2. Yield; 3. field; 4. lie; 5. believe; 6. neighbor; 7. heir; 8. patient; 9. receive; 10. deceived; 11. quiet; 12. friend.

Day 13: pie (a); audience (a); mischief (a); deceit (b); quiet (a); relieved (a); conceited (b); fiend (a); receipt (b); reprieve (a); their (c); view (a); review (a); fierce (a); cashier (a). 1. review (a); 2. mischief (a); 3. quiet (a); 4. audience (a); 5. fierce (a); 6. their (c); 7. cashier (a), receipt (b); 8. relieved (a), reprieve (a); 9. pie (a); 10. fiend (a), conceited (b); 11. view (a).

Day 14: friendly (a); deceitful (b), heirloom (c); unyielded (a); fiendish (a); reprieve (a); patiently (a); relieved (a); conceited (b); audience (a); their (c); quietly (a); viewing (a); thieves (a); belief (a). 1. heirloom (c); 2. relieved (a), fiendish (a), thieves (a); 3. Unyielded (a), deceitful (b), conceited (b), belief (a); 4. viewing (a), audience (a); 5. their (c), friendly (a), quietly (a); 6. patiently (a), reprieve (a).

Day 15: diet (a), eighty (c), pierce (a), siege (a), ceiling (b), shield (a), experience (a), briefcase (a), diesel (a), neighbor (c), tiers (a), pier (a), eighteen (c), sieve (a), niece (a), their (c), unwieldy (a), piety (a); 1. eighteen (c), briefcase (a); 2. diet (a), eighty (c); 3. pierce (a), shield (a); 4. niece (a), experience (a); 5. their (c), ceiling (b); 6. tiers (a), unwieldy (a); 7. siege (a), piety (a); 8. diesel (a), pier (a); 9. neighbor (c); sieve (a).

Day 16: 1. was; 2. was; 3. was; 4. what, wanted, was; 5. what, was; 6. was; 7. what, was; 8. want; 9. was, what, was.

Day 17: Clue: was, -a, -h, want, -h, can't, want, what, what, wh-; Across: 1. was, 3. want, 4. what, 6. want. Down: 1. what, 2. wanted, 4. want, 5. was.

Day 18: 1. what; 2. what; 3. whatever; 4. wants; 5. was; 6. was, was, was; 7. what, what, want; 8. what.

Day 19: 1. what, what; 2. wanting; 3. want; 4. was, was; 5. want; 6. was; 7. what, what, what, what, what, what, what; 8. wanted.

Day 20: Clue: -ai, -a, -e, -ay. Clue: -l, -e, -c, -a, -ei, -ei, -ie. 1. believe, take, reviewing; 2. receive, wait, patiently; 3. faithful, share, believe, saved; 4. pray, neighbors, friends; 5. today, ceiling, spray, away; 6. play, field, rain, May; 7. chief, saved, decades.

Day 21: 1. southbound, doused; 2. astounding, thousand, pounds, flounder (or trout); 3. crouched, pounce, mouse; 4. vouch, doubt, spouse, bounced; 5. wound, hour; 6. house, couch, gout; 7. loud, shout, proudly, trout (or flounder); 8. nouns, (any order:) flour, mouth, ounce, pouch.

Day 22: clue: -ou, -ow; 1. thousand, house; 2. found; 3. devoured, ground; 4. foundation, mountain; 5. counted, found, thousand; 6. counselors; 7. mouth; 8. mountains, fountain, house.

Day 23: 1. hound; 2. mound; 3. round; 4. sound; 5. pout; 6. route; 7. joust; 8. slouch; 9. sour; 10. outcast; 11. foul; 12. ground; 13. mount; 14. countenance; 15. out.

Day 24: across: 1. thou; 2. sour; 4. council; 7. about; 8. grouchy; 9. amount; 12. pounding; 14. doubt; 15. hour; down: 1. trout; 3. vouchers; 4. countenance; 5. louse; 6. abounding; 8. grounded; 10. mouth; 11. pouch; 13. stout.

Day 25: 1. down; 2. cowardly; 3. plowed, Towers, showering, crowded; 4. plowed, power; 5. town, township; 6. Howard, Towers, down, powdery; 7. how, crowds, flowers.

Day 26: 1. drown; 2. drowsiness; 3. brown; 4. town, brow; 5. flower; 6. down, showers, showers; 7. cow, down; 8. bowed down; 9. plowman, plow.

Day 27: 1. chowder; 2. growl; 3. gown; 4. trowel; 5. wow; 6. bow; 7. plow; 8. clown; 9. brown; 10. town; 11. cow; 12. brow; 13. drowsy; 14. powder; 15. power.

Day 28: (Going down) growl, powder, coward, cows, flowers, tower, clown, down, township, shower, chowder, crowded, towel, gown, how, crown.

Day 29: 1. Bowser, hound, bounded, flower, growling, crowds; 2. mounted, round, jousting; 3. chowder, ounce, flour, trout; 4. plowed, house's, foundation, flower; 5. shower, towel, around, brow, foundation, gown; 6. allowed, boughs, owl's; 7. spouse, pouted, about, township, cows, ground; 8. proudly, counted, out, thousand, down, townhouse.

Page 156

Day 30: clue: was, -a, -h; want, -h, can't, want; what, what, wh-; clue: -ai-, -a, -e, -ay; 1. what, was; 2. wait; 3. made, wanted, take, hair; 4. was, motivated, Gabe, play, complaint, today; 5. praised; 6. day, played, rain, made; 7. made, want.

Day 31: one, two, three, four, five, six, seven, eight, nine, ten, eleven, twelve.

Clue 32: clue: one, two, three, four, five, six, seven, eight, nine, ten, eleven, twelve; 1. two, four; 2. one; 3. three; 4. four; 5. twelve; 6. seven, two, five; 7. six, seven; 8. eight; 9. nine; 10. ten, ten, five; 11. four; 12. two; 13. twelve, eleven; 14. four, ten, one, one.

Clue 33: 1. one, four, two, three; 2. nine; 3. two; 4. ten, five; 5. four; 6. twelve; 7. five, five; 8. eight; 9. seven, eleven; 10. six; 11. twelve, twelve; 12. eleven; 13. one, two, one, one, two, two.

Clue 34: 1. one; 2. one, two, three; 3. three; 4. five, two; 5. four; 6. four; 7. six, seven; 8. eight; 9. ten, nine; 10. eleven;11. twelve, twelve.

Clue 35: 1. boy; 2. joy; 3. annoy, annoy; 4. Roy; 5. cloy; 6. soy; 7. coy; 8. ploy; 9. toy; 10. employ.

Clue 36: clue: ends, -oy, middle, -oi-; 1. coin, noise; 2. oil, moist; 3. noise, voice; 4. poise; 5. toils, soil; 6. boiled, broiled; 7. foil, spoil; 8. point, joint; 9. moisture; 10. poinsettia, poisonous.

Clue 37: across: 2. exploit; 5. poinsettia; 7. Detroit; 9. joist; 11. broil; 13. void; 14. soil; 15. coiled; down: 1. poised; 3. point; 4. moisture; 5. poison; 6. choice; 8. toils; 10. spoil; 12. oil.

Day 38: 1. avoid; 2. boil; 3. broil; 4. choice; 5. coil; 6. coin; 7. Detroit; 8. exploit; 9. foil; 10. join; 11. joist; 12. loin; 13. moist; 14. moisture; 15. noise; 16. oil; 17. point; 18. poise; 19. poison; 20. soil; 21. spoil; 22. toil; 23. voice; 24. void.

Day 39: 1. boil, ointment; 2. point; 3. poison; 4. boys; 5. joy; 6. rejoice; 7. joyful, noise; 8. voice; 9. anointed, oil.

Day 40: clue: -ou, -ow; clue: -l, -e, -c, -a, -ei, -ei, -ie; 1. township, our, friends, neighbors; 2. crowds, shout, their, bounce, fields; 3. proudly, believes; 4. counseling, about, retrieve; 5. pouting, mouthing, deceitfulness, allowed; 6. amounts, veins, astounding.

Day 41: (going down...) patted, clapped, skipped, hopped, patting, clapping, skipping, hopping; 1. clapping; 2. hopped; 3. patted; 4. skipping; 5. slipped; (going down...) chatting, hanging, parting, spitting, singing, clipping, shipping, feeling, sleeping, slapping, shopping, trimming.

Day 42: clue: suffix, consonant, short, double; 1. (going down...) grabbed, mopped, budded, wedded, grabbing, mopping, budding, wedding; 2. 1) slipped; 2) clapped; 3) grabbed; 4) hopping; 5) slapped; 6) slipped; 7) begging; 8) slopping; 9) begged; 10) hugged.

Day 43: 1. (going down...) clubbed, subbed, pinned, tripped, jammed, clubbing, subbing, pinning, tripping, jamming; 2. (going down...) b,a,a,a,a,a,b,a,b,b,b,a

Day 44: 1. (Going down...) compelling, forgetting, kidnapping, combatting, abetting, hobnobbing, upsetting, baby-sitting, expelling, abutting, committing, humbugging; 2. (going down...) rapped, kicked, knotted, pulled, chilled, patted, clipped, clumped, chapped, checked, capped, rocked, skinned, shopped, bibbed.

Day 45: 1. 1. clapping (A), waving (c); 2. digging (a), potting (a); 3. chopped (a), camping (b); 4. forgetting (a), striving (c); 5. chipped (a), skinned (a); (going down...) slugged, chipped, robbed, strummed, slugging, chipping, robbing, strumming.

Day 46: (going down...) 1. -y, -I, -ed; babied, married, hurried, worried, accompanied, sanctified, prettied, carried, buried, tarried, cried, occupied, justified, dirtied; 2. -y, -I, -er; merrier, carrier, heavier, stinkier, lovelier, fluffier, friendlier, runnier, happier, sloppier, prettier, uglier, dirtier, stubbier; 3. -y, -I, -es; babies, spies, families, puppies, pennies, lobbies, companies, enemies, cries, ladies, parties, mommies, hippies, cabbies, industries, cities.

Day 47: clue: -y, -y, -I, suffix; (going down...) 1. -y, -I, -est; merriest, grouchiest, heaviest, stinkiest, loveliest, fluffiest, friendliest, funniest, runniest, happiest, sloppiest, prettiest, ugliest, dirtiest, stubbiest, dizziest; 2. -y, -I, -es; candies, cherries, ponies, bellies, buggies, pities, strawberries, flies, pansies, stories, replies, satisfies; 3. strawberries, cherries; 4. loveliest, ponies, buggies; 5. dirtiest, flies.

Day 48: Clue: change, -y, -I, change, -y, -I; (going down...) 1. change -y, vowels; played, deployed, employed, monkeyed, honeyed, prayed, obeyed, frayed, grayed, strayed, moneyed, toyed, replayed, enjoyed; 2. change -y, vowels; player, grayer, employer, sprayer, buyer, prayer; 3. change, -y; plays, bays, sprays, monkeys, honeys, prays, trolleys, joys, valleys, frays, keys, strays, donkeys, toys, guys, obeys, chimneys, repays.

Day 49: 1. (Going down...) playing spraying obeying, straying, replaying, displaying, copying, justifying, hurrying, marrying, accompanying, employing, pitying, paying, praying, fraying, toying, enjoying, graying, trying, crying, carrying, flying, ferrying, burying, partying; 2. -y, -I; not, -I, -I's; not, -y, -I, -i.

Day 50: clue: -y, -y, -I, suffix, change, -y, -I, change, -y, I; clue: suffix, consonant, short, double, rules: -y, -I; not, -y, -I, vowels; not, -y, -I, -I; suffix, consonant, short, double; (going down...) monkeys, kitties, ponies, babies, Sundays, carrying, hurrying, hopping, tipping, pitying, patted, slipped, jumped, popped, checked.

Day 51: 1. explode; 2. choke; 3. stroke; 4. rode; 5. cone; 6. rose; 7. robe; 8. grove; 9. bones; 10. mole; 11. pope, Rome; 12. remote; 13. cloves; 14. note; 15. slope.

Day 52: clue: -o, -e, -oa, -ow, -o, -oe; across: 1. dote; 4. alone; 5. wove; 6. suppose; 8. those; 11. rote; 15. vote; 16. hose; 17. trombone; down: 2. telephone; 3. cove; 5. wrote; 6. strobe; 7. strove; 9. strode; 10.. quote; 12. tote; 13. abode; 14. gnome.

Day 53: 1. close, broke; 2. rose, smoke, smoke; 3. hope, hope; 4. home; 5. chose, stones; 6. ropes; 7. alone; 8. bones, broken; 9. throne.

Day 54: 1. toast; 2. load; 3. toad; 4. oak; 5. soap; 6. oats; 7. Joan; 8. boar; 9. croak; 10. loan; 11. bloat; 12. hoax; 13. throat; 14. moat; 15. boat.

Day 55: 1. coasting; 2. coal; 3. coat, cloak; 4. goads; 5. goat; 6. bemoan; 7. oath; 8. oar; 9. foal; 10. foams.

Day 56: 1. roaming; 2. floats; 3. gloat; 4. road; 5. soar; 6. coax; 7. loaf; 8. soaked; 9. boasting; 10. roast; 11. goal; 12. groan; 13. roar; 14. toast; 15. moan; 16. oatmeal.

Day 57: 1. snow; 2. stow; 3. yoyo; 4. crow; 5. foe; 6. know; 7. bow; 8. hoe; 9. go; 10. show; 11. Joe; 12. tow; 13. pro; 14. flow.

Day 58: 1. throw; 2. blow; 3. toe; 4. glow; 5. quo; 6. no; 7. grow; 8. low; 9. woe; 10. mow; 11. row; 12. so; 13. sow; 14. slow.

Day 59: 1. those, smote, coasts; 2. spoken, cloak; 3. goat, whole; 4. goat, remote, goat, go; 5. bemoan; 6. oath, swore; 7. oath, know; 8. throws, foams.

Page 158

Day 60: clue: ends, -oy, middle, -oi; clue: one, two, three, four, five, six, seven, eight, nine, ten, eleven, twelve; 1. eight, boys, toys; 2. twelve, foil, coiled; 3. three, Joy; 4. rejoices, four; 5. voice, joyful, noise; 6. two, one, moist, soil, royal.

Day 61: 1. Haul; 2. authority; 3. applaud; 4. gaudy; 5. pauper; 6. taught; 7. caught; 8. exhaust; 9. caution; 10. trauma; 11. pause; 12. nauseous; 13. sauce; 14. author; 15. faucet.

Day 62: clue: -au, -aw; 1. applause, 2. plausible; 3. sauna; 4. clause; 5. gauze; 6. caustic; 7. taut; 8. cause; 9. daub; 10. caution; 11. exhausted; 12. bauble.

Day 63: 1. awesome; 2. awl; 3. draw, draw; 4. dawn; 5. jaw; 6. straw; 7. raw; 8. saw; 9. law; 10. paw, paw.

Day 64: 1. August; 2. naughty; 3. authentic; 4. daughter; 5. sausage; 6. saunter; 7. fault; 8. autumn; 9. daunting; 10. auspicious; 11. augment; 12. because; 13. undaunted; 14. faultless; 15. Saul, Paul.

Day 65: (Going down the Scriptures...) law, daughter, lawlessness, haughty, faults, cause, authority, jawbone.

Day 66: forty, one-hundred-twenty, thirty.

Day 67: clue: twenty, thirty, forty, fifty, sixty, seventy, eighty, ninety, hundred, thousand; four-thousand; eight-hundred-fifty; seventy.

Day 68: one-hundred-sixty; eighty; one-hundred-forty.

Day 69: two-thousand-ninety; fifty; one-hundred-thirty.

Day 70: clue: -o, -e, -oa, -ow, -o, -oe. Clue: one, two, three, four, five, six, seven, eight, nine, ten, eleven, twelve. 1. trombone, piano, eight; 2. four, cones, coats; 3. hope, one; 4. two, five, toes; 5. nose, froze, snow; 6. go; 7. suppose, home.

Day 71: 1. spree; 2. teen; 3. creep; 4. peep; 5. sweep; 6. career; 7. cheese; 8. wheel; 9. bleed; 10. sheet; 11. sleek; 12. reek; 13. weeds; 14. cheer; 15. sleeve.

Day 72: clue: -ee, -ea. 1. weeping, feet; 2. flee; 3. free, free, indeed; 4. greet; 5. seeds; 6. heed, keep; 7. sheep; 8. deep, sleep; 9. meek.

Day 73: 1. fleet, 2. agree; 3. street; 4. creed; 5. need; 6. freeze; 7. kneel; 8. tree; 9. week; 10. beep; 11. green; 12. beef.

Day 74: 1. greet; 2. sleet; 3. greed; 4. steed; 5. Greek; 6. reef; 7. weep; 8. teeth; 9. feel; 10. sweet; 11. jeer; 12. meet; 13. three; 14. speed; 15. feed; 16. veer.

Day 75: 1. cheat; 2. treat; 3. bead; 4. steam; 5. rear; 6. tear; 7. cheap; 8. teal; 9. bean; 10. plead; 11. mean; 12. neat; 13. lean; 14. veal; 15. clear.

Day 76: 1. reaping, wheat; 2. streams, season, leaf; 3. lead, teach; 4. fear, clean; 5. beast, speak; 6. hear, ear, peace, tears; 7. near; 8. eat.

Day 77: across: 2. heal; 6. stream; 8. spear; 9. steam; 10. beak; 12. weak; 13. speak; 14. clearly. Down: 1. teams; 3. hear; 4. streak; 5. beam; 7. leak; 11. easy.

Day 78: 1. beat; 2. heat; 3. meat; 4. meal; 5. east; 6. repeat; 7. beam; 8. cream; 9. dream; 10. glean; 11. ream; 12. seam; 13. heap; 14. leap; 15. dear.

Day 79: 1. flea; 2. flee; 3. meet; 4. meat; 5. beat; 6. beet; 7. read; 8. reed; 9. peak; 10. peek; 11. week; 12. weak; 13. heel; 14. heal; 15. real; 16. reel; 17. steel; 18. steal; 19. sea; 20. see.

Day 80: clue: was, -a, -h, want, -h, can't, want, what, what, wh-. Clue: -au, -aw. Clue: -ou, -ow. 1. was, dawn, bound, found, sausage, thawing; 2. wanted; 3. paw, raw, caught; 4. saw, what, was, taught, out, house; 5. howled, undaunted, naughty.

Day 81: 1. loom; 2. swoon; 3. mood; 4. school; 5. cool; 6. shoot; 7. coop; 8. root; 9. moon; 10. noon; 11. spoon; 12. loop; 13. stoop; 14. room; 15. proof.

Day 82: clue: -oo, u-silent-e, -ew, -ue. 1. food; 2. roof; 3. fool; 4. tool; 5. soon; 6. wool; 7. room; 8. gloom, noonday; 9. choose; 10. roots.

Day 83: 1. zoo; 2. brood; 3. moo; 4. shoo; 5. goofy; 6. aloof; 7. pool; 8. spool; 9. broom; 10. droop; 11. hoop; 12. troops; 13. boot; 14. tooth; 15. groom; 16. raccoon.

Day 84: 1. cube; 2. rude; 3. dude; 4. June; 5. plume; 6. prune; 7. dune; 8. tune; 9. brute; 10. chute; 11. cute; 12. utensil; 13. resume; 14. include; 15. accuse; 16. mute; 17. confuse.

Day 85: 1. rude; 2. mule; 3. rule; 4. ruler; 5. disputed; 6. refuse; 7. prunes; 8. lukewarm; 9. refuge; 10. accuser.

Day 86: 1. few; 2. chew; 3. Jew; 4. mew; 5. drew; 6. new; 7. pew; 8. flew; 9. dew; 10. knew; 11. stew; 12. grew; 13. brew; 14. blew; 15. crew.

Day 87: 1. glue; 2. imbue; 3. blue; 4. true; 5. clue; 6. hue; 7. due; 8. Sue; 9. cue; 10. fluent; 11. accrue; 12. ensue.

Day 88: 1. chew; 2. blew; 3. dew; 4. blue; 5. few; 6. Jews; 7. new; 8. knew; 9. Sue; 10. grew; 11. stew; 12. true.

Day 89: across; 4. true; 5. chew; 7. crew; 8. flue; 9. Sue; 11. drew; 12. Jew. Down: 1. stew; 2. due; 3. accrue; 6. blue; 7. clue; 8. flew; 10. grew.

Day 90: clue: -y, -y, -I, suffix; change, -y, -I; change, -y, -i. clue: -au, -aw. Clue: ends, -oy; middle, -oi. 1. boy's, voice, squawked, tried, ladies; 2. raucous, noisily, awning, caught, August; 3. cities; spoiled; saunter, awful; 4. daughter, faucet, boil, pastries, enjoyment.

Day 91: (going down...) bright, right, light, fight, tight, sight. 1. light; 2. sight; 3. fight; 4. bright; 5. right; 6. tight; 7. right, fight; 8. bright, light; 9. tight, sight.

Day 92: clue: i-silent-e, -y, ends, -ight, -gh. (going down...) blight, fright, might, flight, plight, night. 1. plight; 2. might; 3. night; 4. blight; 5. flight; 6. fright; 7. blight, plight; 8. might, flight; 9. night, fright.

Day 93: 1. midnight; 2. right; 3. lightbulb; 4. mighty; 5. bright; 6. sight; 7. fight; 8. tight; 9. flight; 10. blighted.

Day 94: across: 1. mighty; 2. Dwight; 5. lightbulb; 8. flight; 9. tight; 10. blight. Down: 1. midnight; 3. sight; 4. plight; 6. brightly; 7. right; 8. fright.

Day 95: 1. strike; 2. wire; 3. five; 4. dime; 5. hike; 6. shine; 7. chime; 8. wife; 9. fire; 10. mice; 11. slide; 12. ice; 13. vine; 14. alive; 15. kite.

Page 160

Day 96: 1. hide; 2. pride, life; 3. defile; 4. abide; 5. wise, time; 6. like, fire; 7. bride, wife; 8. vine; 9. like, white.

Day 97: across: 1. swine; 4. incline; 6. confide; 7. ice; 8. entice; 9. knife. Down: 1. strike; 2. refine; 3. Nile; 5. chive; 6. confine.

Day 98: 1. bribe; 2. rice; 3. suffice; 4. twice; 5. wide; 6. spine; 7. price; 8. pile; 9. lime; 10. smile; 11. tribe; 12. slime; 13. nine; 14. tire; 15. mile.

Day 99: 1. wife, bite, slice, lime; 2. shine, grime, smiles; 3. why, try, surprise, fine; 4. pry, pine, pipe, bike; 5. Nile, miles, side; 6. wise, price, nine, kite.

Day 100: (going down...) hopped, jumped, skipped, smiled, camped, pinned, tanned, flipped, hated, sinned, parted, begged, one-hundred-forty; two-hundred-eighty.

Day 101: 1. why, does; 2. only; 3. who; 4. who, does; 5. why, only; 6. does; 7. does; 8. only; 9. who; 10. only.

Day 102: clue: -h, do, -es, long –o, -w, two, -w. 1. why; 2. does, who; 3. only; 4. does; 5. who, only; 6. why; 7. does; 8. why, does; 9. only, who; 10. who, why.

Day 103: 1. does, does; 2. only; 3. who; 4. why; 5. does; 6. why; 7. does; 8. only; 9. who; 10. why.

Day 104: 1. why, does; 2. only, does, 3. who; 4. does, who; 5. why; 6. who; 7. why; 8. only; 9. why; 10. does, only.

Day 105: 1. only, does; 2. why, does; 3. who; 4. does; 5. who; 6. why; 7. does; 8. only; 9. only; 10. why, who.

Day 106: Your address will go in the upper left-hand corner of all three envelopes. 1. Your grandparent's address would go in the center. 2. Your friend's address will go in the center. 3. Your out-of-state friend or relative's address will go in the center.

Day 107: Clue: return, left, N-, S-, T-, S-, capitalized, (.). Your address will go in the upper left-hand corner of all three envelopes. 1. The address of another friend will go in the center. 2. Your cousin's address will go in the center. 3. Your church's address will go in the center.

Day 108: Your address will go in the upper left-hand corner of all three envelopes. 1. A missionary's address will go in the center. 2. Your local electric company's address will go in the center. 3. Your parents' address will go in the center (same address in the left hand corner *and* the center, except your name will be in the return address [left corner] and your parents' names in the center).

Day 109: Your address will go in the upper left-hand corner of all three envelopes. 1. Another cousin's address will go in the center. 2. The address of another out-of-state friend or relative will go in the center. 3. Your neighbor's address will go in the center.

Day 110: clue: -ee, -ea. Clue: -o, -e; -oa, -ow, -o, -oe. 1. home, sweet, home; 2. grow, beans, peas, oats; 3. sheep, coats, snow, week; 4. steam, boat, sea; 5. please, phone.

Day 111: 1. dangerous; 2. famous; 3. jealous; 4. momentous; 5. porous; 6. barbarous; 7. bulbous; 8. copious; 9. humorous; 10. joyous; 11. obvious; 12. continuous.

Day 112: clue: -ous, -cious, -tious. 1. prosperous; 2. generous; 3. glorious; 4. courageous; 5. jealous, jealous; 6. miraculous; 7. various; 8. righteous; unrighteous; 9. anxious.

Day 113: across: 3. vigorous; 4. stupendous; 6. marvelous; 7. joyous; 8. raucous; 10. odious; 11. ominous. Down: 1. studious; 2. erroneous; 3. victorious; 5. serious; 9. curious.

Day 114: 1. obnoxious; 2. nauseous; 3. hazardous; 4. unscrupulous; 5. tedious; 6. ponderous; 7. poisonous; 8. generous; 9. infamous; 10. tremendous; 11. envious; 12. cantankerous.

Day 115: 1. spacious; 2. vicious; 3. suspicious; 4. pernicious; 5. delicious; 6. voracious; 7. vivacious; 8. precious; 9. ferocious; 10. gracious; 11. malicious; 12. conscious; 13. tenacious.

Day 116: 1. rambunctious; 2. facetious; 3. cautious; 4. infectious; 5. contentious; 6. fictitious; 7. fractious; 8. ostentatious; 9. nutritious; 10. licentious; 11. vexatious.

Day 117: 1. precious; 2. gracious, gracious; 3. malicious; 4. contentious; 5. deliciously.

Day 118: 1. spacious; 2. precious; 3. suspicious; 4. delicious; 5. conscious; 6. vicious; 7. cautious; 8. nutritious; 9. fictitious; 10. voracious.

Day 119: 1. notorious; 2. ridiculous; 3. harmonious; 4. numerous; 5. previous; 6. nervous; 7. rebellious; 8. disastrous; 9. monstrous; 10. fastidious; 11. virtuous; 12. righteous; 13. gorgeous; 14. callous.

Day 120: clue: i-silent-e, -y, ends, -ight, -gh. Clue: -oo, -u-silent-e, -ew, -ue. 1. night, June, coon, moon; 2. brute, frightened, dude, mule; 3. groom, disputed, bright, light; 4. blue, might, bloom, cool; 5. include, ruler, school; 6. glue, loop, tightly.

Day 121: 1. influence; 2. experience; 3. independence; 4. eloquence; 5. intelligence; 6. patience; 7. presence; 8. obedience; 9. violence; 10. innocence; 11. preference; 12. circumference; 13. confidence; 14. negligence; 15. correspondence.

Day 122: clue: -ence, -ance. 1. resistance; 2. countenance; 3. circumstance; 4. vengeance; 5. ignorance; 6. perseverance; 7. inheritance; 8. entrance; 9. sustenance; 10. extravagance; 11. grievance; 12. importance; 13. dissonance; 14. dominance; 15. repentance.

Day 123: 1. conscience; 2. patience, temperance; 3. presence; 4. ignorance; 5. confidence; 6. countenance; 7. violence.

Day 124: Across: 3. ignorance; 7. pestilence; 8. grievance; 9. preeminence. Down: 1. preference; 2. benevolence; 4. negligence; 5. obedience; 6. science.

Day 125: (going down...) puncture, legislature, furniture, miniature, literature, rapture, dentures, lecture, featured, adventure. 1. dentures; 2. miniature; 3. literature; 4. rapture; 5. lecture; 6. featured; 7. puncture; 8. furniture.

Day 126: clue: -ture. Across: 1. literature; 3. signature; 4. future; 5. creature; 6. furniture; 8. adventure; 10. torture; 11. lecture. Down: 1. legislature; 2. rapture; 4. feature; 6. fracture; 7. indenture; 9. nurture.

Day 127: (going down...) tortured, pictures, nature, nurture, Scripture, furniture, pasture, creature, future. 1. furniture; 2. pasture; 3. pictures; 4. future; 5. creature; 6. nurture; 7. Scripture; 8. tortured; 9. nature.

Day 128: (going down...) tincture, miniature, fixture, suture, indenture, mature, literature, adventures, departure, featured. 1. adventures; 2. featured; 3. fixture; 4. mature; 5. suture, tincture; 6. miniature; 7. departure.

Page 162

Day 129: tortured, adventure, mature, legislature, captured, lectured, Scripture, signature, future.

Day 130: clue: i-silent-e, -y, ends, -ight, -gh. Clue: -h, do, -es, long -o, -w, two, -w. Clue: -ee, -ea. 1. why, does, scream, time; 2. only, eats, beef, pie. 3. who, bike, knees; 4. does, price, tires, deal; 5. why, does, queen, bee, leave, hive.

Day 131: (going down...) -o-, -o-, -wi, -i-, -a-, wi-, -a-, woul-, woul-, -o-, ha-, a-, ha-, -o-, wi-, a-; 1. don't, you're; 2. you'll; 3. could've; 4. wouldn't; 5. they'll; 6. that's, you'd; 7. she'd.

Day 132: clue: two, one, missing, doesn't, squeezed, taken out. Used to be, spell, change, used to be. 1. didn't; 2. don't, isn't, he'll; 3. he's; 4. we're; 5. I'm; 6. I've.

Day 133: (going down...) doesn't (o), we've (ha), they've (ha), I'd (woul), he's (i), we'll (wi), hasn't (o), who's (i), can't (no), weren't (o), we're (a), they'd (woul), I'm (a), who'll (wi), they're (a), you'll (wi). 1. there's; 2. nothing's; 3. I'll; 4. it's; 5. he'll 6. it's; 7. we've.

Day 134: (going down...) aren't (o), shouldn't (o), she's (i), who'll (wi), we'll (wi), they're (a), we'd (woul), haven't (o), hasn't (o), it's (i), they'll (wi), we're (a), I'd (woul), you're (a). 1. wouldn't; 2. you're; 3. we've; 4. aren't; 5. they're; 6. isn't; 7. don't, it's.

Day 135: 1. curfew; 2. hurt; 3. spurt; 4. burr; 5. blurry; 6. curl; 7. unfurl; 8. nurse; 9. burn; 10. turf; 11. murky; 12. churn; 13. surf; 14. turkey; 15. burp.

Day 136: clue: -ur, -ir, -er. 1. shirt; 2. dirt; 3. girder; 4. thirty; 5. bird; 6. stir; 7. third; 8. girl; 9. sir; 10. swirl; 11. birch; 12. shirk; 13. firm; 14. squirm; 15. chirp.

Day 137: 1. her; 2. derby; 3. verb; 4. term; 5. perfume; 6. perfect; 7. iceberg; 8. germ; 9. perch; 10. thermal; 11. Germany; 12. fern; 13. verse; 14. nerve; 15. permanent.

Day 138: 1. skirt; 2. thirsty; 3. murder; 4. lurk; 5. furry; 6. permanent; 7. concern; 8. person; 9. flirt; 10. squirt; 11. curse; 12. fervent.

Day 139: 1. adversary, firm; 2. first; 3. murder; 4. curse; 5. church, purchased; 6. perfume; 7. fervent; 8. purpose.

Day 140: clue: -ous, -cious, -tious. Clue: -ence, -ance. Clue: -ture. 1. instance, audience, lecture, silence; 2. difference, assurance, presence, anxious. 3. nature, dangerous, glorious, violence, radiance.

Day 141: 1. should; 2. should; 3. would; 4. would; 5. could; 6. could; 7. could.

Day 142: clue: -ould. 1. could; 2. should; 3. could; 4. would; 5. should; 6. should; 7. would, would.

Day 143: 1. would; 2. could; 3. should; 4. could; 5. should, should; 6. could; 7. would, would, would, would.

Day 144: (going down...) edge, dredge, hedge, pledge, grudge, fudge, judge, lodge, nudge. 1. pledge; 2. judge; 3. fudge; 4. nudge; 5. lodge; 6. hedge; 7. dredge; 8. edge; 9. grudge.

Day 145: Clue: -j, -dge. 1. badge; 2. drudge; 3. budget; 4. dredge; 5. sledge; 6. midget; 7. gadget; 8. grudge; 9. hodgepodge; 10. edge; 11. smudge; 12. bridge.

Day 146: (going down...) badger, hedge, pledge, edge, judge, lodge, grudge, ledges, wedge. 1. judge, judge; 2. edge; 3. grudge; 4. hedge; 5. lodge, lodge; 6. pledge; 7. badger; 8. ledges, ledges; 9. wedge.

Day 147: 1. pitch; 2. match; 3. catch; 4. witch; 5. crutch; 6. watch; 7. batch; 8. fetch; 9. scratch; 10. Dutch; 11. ditch; 12. patch.

Day 148: Clue: -j, -dge, -ch, -tch. 1. bench; 2. watch; 3. fetch; 4. finch; 5. crutch; 6. botch; 7. much; 8. match; 9. wretch; 10. hitch; 11. bunch; 12. pinch; 13. catch; 14. which, witch, which.

Day 149: 1. torch, porch, church, birch; 2. hunch, punch, lunch, stretch; 32. watch, clutch, lurch, flinch; 4. crunch, latch, munch, scratch.

Day 150: clue: -ous, -cious, -tious. Clue: two, one, missing, doesn't, squeezed, taken out, used to be, spell, change, used to be. Clue: -ur, -ir, -er. 1. turkey, can't, delicious, nutritious; 2. isn't, raucous, girl, curly, thirty; 3. purple, shirt, doesn't, gorgeous, skirt; 4. I'll, nervous, dangerous, derby; 5. ridiculous, nurse, didn't, germs, dirty.

Congratulations! You did it!

Ordering Information

Schoolhouse Publishing has many unique and wonderful books to enhance your student's academic progress. Our books are easy to use, enjoyable, require little or no teacher preparation, and are widely acclaimed. Below is a sample of some of our popular books:

- *Apples Daily spelling Drills for Secondary Students*
- *Apples 2 Daily Phonics Drills for Secondary Students*
- *Research in Increments*
- *Word Artist*
- *The Creative Writing Score Card*
- *Revolution*
- *Pennsylvania Keystones*

For a complete catalog, call 215-721-9293, and leave your name, telephone number, and address. Or, check out our website:

www.shpublishing.com